# CULTURE
## CULT

### ANTHOLOGY

CultureCult Anthology
**SPECIALS**

# LOCKDOWN LITERATURE

EDITED BY
JAY CHAKRAVARTI

CULTURE
**CULT**
PRESS

LOCKDOWN LITERATURE
Anthology of Poetry, Fiction and Non Fiction
Edited by: Jay Chakravarti

First Printing, 2020

ISBN: 9798583863075

**CultureCult Press**
www.CultureCult.co.in

Published by:
Jagannath (Jay) Chakravarti,
11/1, Khanpur Road,
Kolkata 700047
West Bengal, India

# CONTENTS

## NON FICTION

14   FRANCES GUERIN - *Grieving*
22   C.H.WILLIAMS - *Transition*

## FICTION

32   NATHAN BAKER - *Locked In*
42   BAREERAH GHANI - *Caged*
47   MALCOLM BARCLAY - *We Don't Stop*
63   JAMES R. GAPINSKI - *The Fortune Teller's Grand Re-Opening*
71   LEE CROSS - *My Friend The...*
78   DIANE PAYNE - *Why?*
81   RICH LARSON - *Samsung Syndrome*
88   BARNALI SAHA - *A Flatbread Story*
98   MALAVIKA V R - *Four Worlds and a Pandemic*
103  NILES REDDICK - *Shallow Water*
107  ZÉLIA DE SOUSA - *Really?*
108  ELIZABETH ROBYN STANTON - *The Day we Learned to Wash our Hands*
112  ANINDITA SARKAR - *Praying for Recovery*
115  KAMAL ABDUL NASIR - *Long Pause*

## POETRY - Pg 125 to 210

*Alan Perry, Ann Privateer, Baisali Chatterjee Dutt, Bhisma Upreti (Translation Rupsingh Bhandari), Dr.Brajesh Kumar Gupta "Mewadev", Christian Garduno, Colleen Moyne, Dimple D. Mapari, Donna Nemmers, Donny Winter, Drew Pisarra, Ed O'Casey, Edilson Afonso Ferreira, Emilian Lungu, George R. Ross / Vitoria Crawford, H.L. Dowless, Hilary King, Howie Good, Jane Carter, Jared Morningstar, Jay Gandhi, Karol*

*Nielsen, Katley Demetria Brown, Kelly Nickie, LA Felleman, Linda Scheller, Lita Kurth, Lynn White, Mark Blickley (Image by Beatrice Georgalidis), Meg Smith, Megha Sood, O. Yemi Tubi (MOYAT), P.J. Reed, Preksha Kukreja, Rich Larson, Richard C. Enos, Robert Allen, Dr. Ron Craig, Sanchari Chatterjee, Soumyadeep Roy, Subhranil Mahato, Suchita Parikh-Mundul, Sueann Wells, Suparna Chaudhury Rijhwani, Vandana Kumari Jena, Zélia De Sousa*

**202 - POET BIOGRAPHIES**

# FOREWORD

My year had started on the wrong note to begin with. Struggling with my inner selves, shacked up in a hotel room in wintry Mushidabad, I was as far away from my loved ones as Bengal's erstwhile capital was from its majestic Nawabi days.

Even after returning to Kolkata, my tribulations were not over before an extended stay at a place meant to placate the disturbed. The stay both helped and did not. On the one hand, I was out of the extended state of battle that I was lodging with my inner selves, whose inevitable effects were troubling the people around me, especially my mother. Yet, I found myself back to square one when it came to the persona that happened to be my sense of the self. I was an irredeemable bundle of uncertainties still regarding almost every aspect of my life.

Round the time Covid had started snaking its way into people's lives, gradually taking over the headlines of daily news, I, along with most of my fellow Indians, were blissfully unaware of the sheer magnitude that this crisis was about to evolve into. In fact, for only the second time in my life, I found myself accepting a full-time job come March.

I have been averse to a regular job ever since I left college. My publication venture apart, I would do the occasional freelance direction jobs that came my way. In 2016, I had briefly taken up a regular teaching job which I had to quit following payment issues on the employers'' end. This 2020 job at a marketing agency was only the 2nd time I had accepted a full time position in my life.

More than the money, months of binging on The Office had created in me a craving for experiencing a proper office job. I love to teach, but even big classrooms and a dedicated teacher's room fell short of being a proper "office" experience.

Thus began my three-week stint in an office which soon shut down as Corona came to India and the whole nation retreated into a state of lockdown.

At a period of time when people around the world began losing their jobs, I was battling the dangerously depressing lockdown with a new job and work-from-home sessions that helped me keep my nerves in check to a certain extent.

And there were just so many issues going on all around with the potential of derailing one's centre of gravity! First there was the fear of contracting the coronavirus itself. More than the 14-day quarantine and the associated symptoms (among which difficulty of breathing was the most worrisome), there was the fear of being isolated by one and all, which would spell a deep crisis for the innumerable stray cats and dogs that find shelter in our home.

Deaths around the world did not spare our house, even though Covid had nothing to do with it. In April, my family lost two of the first dogs we had adopted some twelve years ago, the big and happy *Naru* and the lovable *Joey*, the one with the kangaroo ears.

The tragedy of their deaths fresh in our minds, Kolkata was struck by the cyclone *Amphan* in May. The fierce winds knocked down the tin-covers over our rooftop and put in a blind little fear of winds and rains in me that will last at least until next year.

Matters on the homefront were constantly being augmented by the workings of what was happening in the rest of the globe. The plight of the migrant workers, who were walking hundreds of kilometres to get back home and dying likes flies in the process. The baby playing with the *anchal* of the dead mother's *saree* on a railway platform. Oh, ghastly images!

I lost my maternal grandmother on September the 5th. She passed away barely hours after we got to see her after months; years for me.

This year has renewed the meaning of "Fear" in my life. Both love and the lack of it have failed to triumph over its sacrilegious all-pervading presence. Death has been a constant, as I sit down to write this editorial after the deaths of two beloved young cats in a span of two days this December.

One good thing about this year has been the opportunity to publish a great number of talented authors. The concept for this Lockdown themed anthology was to partially mark a strange, fearful and frustrating year in human history. From a reader's point of view, I cannot discount the fact that I wanted to know how people like me around the world were coping in these challenging times.

Sensitivity comes at a price, which creative individuals tend to pay with art that is intensely personal and universal at the same time. It has been nothing short of a privilege to read the real and fictional stories & poems that 2020 has been able to conjure off the bunch of talented artistes featured in this anthology.

It has been wondrous to find people expressing emotions as diverse as hope, grief, anger as well as love to describe their experience of lockdown 2020. Here's wishing that you find something valuable among these pages which can help you make sense of this year that is about to end and give you a sense of positivity for the year we are poised to begin. Let our hopes renew as we gingerly tread forth towards a different future to the new normal we have been forced to get accustomed to.

**Jay Chakravarti**
December 11, 2020
Editor, Lockdown Literature

# LOCKDOWN LITERATURE

*Anthology of Poetry, Fiction & Non Fiction*

# NON FICTION

# FRANCES GUERIN

# GRIEVING

A tightness has settled permanently in my chest. I say settled, but it migrates, independently, without permission, between throat and chest, sometimes venturing down to my belly.

We are now in an advanced stage of grieving. Otherwise known as re-opening. Our mourning commenced with the non-arrival of what became known as "the new normal." The new was scheduled to spring up in the shadow of death. We didn't know the old was gone, lost forever, until the newly arrived, itself, failed to show up. Its absence now fills my chest.

I was ecstatic when the President announced that we would be let out of confinement. Even here in Paris, where the numbers had skyrocketed and the hospitals had been overwhelmed, May 11 was to be the magical day. Like many others, I assumed it would be the upward turn following months of depression. I looked at a man sitting on a bench, his hands crossed on his knees, head down, as another rifled through trash further along the street. We all yearned for the city to start moving again.

The long-anticipated celebration never took place; the freedom has never been experienced. Not only did we never go back to anything resembling before, but we are again watching numbers, stalked by a second possible confinement. We have been through the denial, anger, frustration, resignation, guilt. We are meant to be in the hope stage, but we've gone back to grieving for this moment that was meant to be different. It was meant to be familiar, like before. Or, at least, new. Reality is an enduring uncertainty that has migrated into our bodies, a sharp anxiety.

Since de-confinement, I have felt guilty for being European. My American friends are still isolating while I go to museums, the movies, and spend my days at the library. Self-help books tell me that guilt is meant to come before depression. Websites reassure me that the order is irrelevant. Grief doesn't progress in predictable, linear stages. I believe the websites. It's okay to feel guilty.

In Europe, we think of ourselves as survivors. We pulled through the worst of it by obeying the government orders. Recently, *The New York Times* gleefully announced that we have more infections per capita than the United States, but that can't be right. It must be American envy. My guilt and goodwill towards Americans morphs into spite while I am not looking.

If it's not envy, how to explain *The New York Times* article? Maybe the facts and figures read differently on opposite sides of the Atlantic Ocean? Per capita infection rates are higher in densely populated areas, more deaths per rate of infection means higher death rate, more testing means more cases. Is that according to a linear or logarithmic scale?

It's easier to return to identifying as survivors; the alternative is to fall into a state of confusion.

Overwhelmed by graphs and data, I look outside my window to gauge reality. The streets are empty again.Maybe *The New York Times* is right. Are we all self-designating a new isolation?

No. I forgot. It's August in Paris. Everyone has gone to the Cote d'Azur. I naïvely thought that Parisians might work through August this year. So many months lost to the pandemic and all.

"Are you going on vacation?" I ask the man at the bike store.

"Mais madame," he responds with incredulity. "It's August."

"Yes, of course," I sigh.

It's August, and we never made it to a new normal.

I'm waiting for the President to tell us that it's over, that we can move on with our lives, and rekindle hope for the future. We did so well at flattening the curve in the first place. Surely we deserve to relax for the rest of the year?

"The Russians have officially approved a vaccine," I excitedly tell the pharmacist.

"The Russians, the Russians, the Russians are coming," he chants. A smile brushes over his face. "They called it Sputnik," he smirks.

When the new order comes from the French government, it's in the form of a city map. It is a spiderweb of red coloured streets on which mask wearing is obligatory. I anxiously wait for the map to download. C'mon, c'mon. I deflate. My street is red.

I am momentarily reassured because my building is on a corner. If I turn left outside my building, I must wear a mask, but if I turn right, no mask needed. The longer I ponder the map, the more confused I become.

It doesn't make sense. Do I need a mask to cross the street, and take two steps left, then when I turn right onto the boulevard I am allowed to remove the mask? Do I wear it on my bike? The all-important question: will the police be giving out fines to the disobedient? I scour the Préfecture de Police website for answers. Nothing. I look out the window; no one is wearing a mask.

Here we go again.

At least we are not in America where confusion has been elevated to political ideology. In France, confusion pops up in familiar conversations with foreigners who eat outside of the designated hour, try to substitute fries for greens, or want sauce on the side in a restaurant.

I hesitate before writing formal emails to colleagues in America, especially those in states where the virus rages out of control. What do I say? I hope you are keeping well and ignoring your government's instructions to go about business as usual? Delete.

I could have told you there would be a price to pay for all those beach parties and "socially distanced" walks in the park. Delete.

At least in New York you flattened the curve. Delete.

I settle for: I hope you are keeping well.

No judgment, no assumptions about political proclivities, or mask preference. I don't want them to think I'm smug. Even though I am.

Guilt, resentment, compassion with a touch of conceit, I am losing my grasp. What am I meant to be feeling? How am I meant to behave towards others in the middle of a global pandemic? Will someone please write the manual.

The world as we know it has evaporated. Poof. Disappeared over the course of a weekend in March. If only I had known the end was coming. If only I had made the most of my situation, instead of always wanting more, wishing I was somewhere else. If only. If only. I might have prepared for survival of the oncoming unknown instead of scrolling through drivel on Twitter.

I may be in Europe, but there are days when I might as well be in America. I sit in my apartment – again – alone, imagining that everyone else has picked up where their lives left off. They're probably out at dinner, in one of the restaurants that spills over the sidewalk and onto the street. I listen to young people in the bar downstairs, talking, laughing, drinking together until the early hours. I follow friends' Facebook posts and envy their vacations: eating gelati in Italy, swimming in the Sardinian sea, hiking through the Carpathians.

Why aren't they wearing masks? I grumble at the screen.

I sit home, wondering when this will be over and what comes next.

"No one knows," my friend Kate reassures me.

Kate reminds me of how difficult it is for her cellist husband. "The venues are closed until May 2021."

I feel better temporarily. Until Friday.

On Fridays, the anxiety is higher than usual. It begins when I wake. The UK university at which I am employed will be writing to notify me of how

**THE LACEMAKER** *by* **JOHANNES VERMEER**

many million pounds in debt it has fallen this week. The figure grows steadily. There will be too much information about the number of jobs on the line, how many colleagues have agreed to take salary reductions, and the reasons why we should all agree to a pay freeze.

There will be details of the ongoing search for a Public Relations manager, a new Marketing team, a Financial overseer. Academic departments are shrinking, management is bloating. I don't need to know any of this; I am employed to teach the next generation, not to carry the management's guilt for the past ten years of bad investments.

I ignore the emails, until my mind wanders to the question of what I will say to parents at Open Day: sorry, we no longer offer this or that degree, but do send your child to this university because we have a world-class Marketing team.

An email from HR informs us of administrators being made redundant. "They know their jobs are at risk, but it will still come as a shock. Be nice to them." It reminds me of a primer: Help your family in times of grief.

I guess this must be a British thing. The UK government had the same strategy: you need to take responsibility for our mistakes. The slogan plastered to the podium at every press conference comes quickly to mind:"stay home, protect the NHS." Translation: Don't go to hospital if you are sick because the health system is too fragile, thanks to the fact that we have de-funded it.

In Paris, we are privileged. Even when the spread was at its most virulent, we were not reminded of mortality on a daily basis. There were no triages on sidewalks. Ambulance sirens didn't blare around the clock. There were few tangible signs of the virus spreading, no visible panic in the streets, no stories of the dead being buried in mass graves. We respect the dead as much as the living here in Paris, I think. Unlike the university and the British Prime Minister, the French government didn't expect us to be nice to those who suffered as a result of its wrongs.

I worry out loud to my friend Mary about what I will do if I get sick, given that my health relies on the British NHS.

"In France, we have a centralized government," Mary responds.

"What difference does that make?"

"Oh, you know," responds Mary. Clearly, *she* doesn't know.

I have spent too long tethered to events in the UK and realize it's best to go back into denial. Or to the Louvre.

I make the most of the recently open museums by visiting some of my favorite paintings in the Louvre. I shed a tear to be reunited with them; we are like old friends. They are a great comfort to me in this time of transition between confinement and who knows what. I ask them how they cope with this madness, the confinement, isolation, mask wearing, and social distancing.

Reflecting on Vermeer's *The Lacemaker*, I am assured that her life would have gone on as usual in confinement. She would have toiled away at her handwork with only her thoughts for company. In the early stages of de-confinement, she may have made more money than she could spend. She would have been sought after to make masks. We would have all lined up for her services. That is, before the heatwave when we realized how hot it is behind a fabric mask, and how often the fabric masks need to be washed. Then when we all started using the disposable kind that we could throw on the street after use, *The Lacemaker* would have returned to fashioning ladies' lace nothings for the rest of the summer.

Delacroix's *Women of Algiers* would also have thrived in confinement. I imagine the demand for services in the pleasure industry continuing, business as usual, with or without a pandemic. They would have continued to recline on sumptuous cushions, playing games, waiting to receive visitors. I am fairly certain that the patrons of both the *Women of Algiers* and Ingres's *Bathers* would continue their habits during the Coronavirus. It wouldn't seem right to deprive these lovely ladies of business on account of a crazy bat flu.

I am struck by how little difference a global pandemic would make to any of the belles at the Louvre. Luckily for them, shelter in place would be no different from every other day of their lives. The *Mona Lisa* might be the only exception because she is not used to being alone. She probably took the opportunity of a room empty of tourists to sneak into the celebrations on the opposite wall in Veronese's *The Wedding Feast at Cana*. Since the museum opened for de-confinement, it's a different story. She has been removed from display on account of her seduction. She draws too many ogling visitors, the hundreds and millions each day, packed together, jostling for the best perspective of her ambiguous face, risks the spread of the Coronavirus. That said, I am sure she has found a nice man in the conservation department to look at her all day and night. She will be downstairs, wearing her wry smile as if she has the secret to ending this nightmare.

The men are a different story. Little Louis on his horse would have been frustrated and angry at not being able to parade his greatness in front of a crowd of adoring fans. Even Jesus would have yearned for his usual public, his audience of followers, worshippers, disciples.

I am reminded that not all the men are as egocentric as Louis and Jesus when I look at Mantegna's poor *Saint Sebastian*. He is tethered to an ancient column, his body bleeding from the arrows piercing his translucent skin, suffering the same, with or without a crowd, global pandemic or not.

I wish I could take up residence in the Louvre, away from reality, cocooned in the dramas of oil on canvases.

It's Friday again. The president of the university is filled with compassion and care for all of us. She knows how it feels.

"We are all suffering," she writes. "Know that you are not alone."

There is so much compassion in her email that I can almost hear tremulous violin strings.

I sense the pain of Mantegna's *Saint Sebastian*, his body like target practice for the archers, surrounded by death and decay. That's empathy.

I hit Reply All and compose the response, continuing the empty platitudes. Facetiously. "Know that somehow you will survive." "Allow for numbness." "It's okay if the pain never goes away."

I pause before hitting send. This doesn't need to be said by me. I save to draft.

I watch a sheep being shorn in a documentary on television. The animal writhes as the fleece is lifted from its back with an electric razor. One slip of the blades and it could bleed to death. The shearer turns the sheep over and it nuzzles its head into the man's legs for safety.

My anxiety continues. There is no way to take control of the future. I am learning to live with the uncertainty of not knowing. The grief may be here to stay. []

**FRANCES GUERIN** is a professor of art and visual culture at the University of Kent in Paris. She has published five books, many articles, and her essays can be found in Zocalo Public Square, Artslant, Art Houston.

# C.H. WILLIAMS

# TRANSITION

*You can throw away the vial after two doses. Don't bother trying to get that little bit out of the bottom.*

The first week working from home, I feel perpetually nauseous and shaky, because I got a text saying that my next follow-up appointment was cancelled due to the pandemic, and I decide to ignore the clinician's advice. I can get that little bit out of the bottom of both the vials, I can go another week without a new prescription.

I'd only been on testosterone for a month when the world shut down. My throat had been itching from the first injection, teasing at the voice drop that'd come months later, and I had been excitedly hiding lozenges at my desk and sipping honeyed tea.

After my first injection, I called my friends and told them that now, more than ever, I needed our connections. I needed to talk to them often, needed them to partake in these beautiful shifts with me, because my transness is best cultivated with the people I love, and this was a moment of flourishing. Around this time, someone sent me the Julian Jarboe quote that reads, "God blessed me by making me a transsexual for the same reason he made wheat but not bread and fruit but not wine; because he wants humanity to share in the act of creation," and it was champagne bubbles in my chest, because I felt so righteously vindicated for sharing this experience.

My vials of testosterone made me feel like I was getting away with something clever. After a barrage of hurtful remarks—*you're perfectly feminine, I feel like I would be losing something if you started hormones* and other transphobic vitriol—I was able to prioritize my own well-being over my fear of disappointing people who weren't really that invested in my well-being.

So when my next follow-up was cancelled with no new appointment date set, I panicked. I'd fought an uphill battle to be okay with this. Those tiny vials on my dresser represented years of intense emotional work and deep self-love—and the idea that they'd disappear without my consent was mortifying.

23

Lockdown was industrial-grade paint stripper, chipping away at my transitional agency. This had been *my* process. I had dictated the timeline, how I would practice self-acceptance and self-love and patience with my shifting sense of self, but that was always a fragile agency.

They did set another appointment before the prescription ran out and I secured another one-month refill. But everyone else rushed to the pharmacy, either trying to get prescriptions filled while they could, or else just to try and cram as many thermometers and bottles of flu medicine into their baskets as possible. I held up the line for thirty minutes when my insurance refused to cover the prescription, and though I do go back the next day to get it, I am still frustrated about this in spite of the months that have since passed, because this refusal is a symbol for how my transition has been re-routed by the pandemic.

The trouble with being trans is that I have not been permitted any difficulty with my transition. To admit that parts of it are rocky is to open the door to people demanding to know why I would do this to myself if it's unpleasant; to say that it is going perfectly negates the rough waters that are just part of life, and ignores the ways in which cisnormative culture makes transitioning difficult. Lockdown amplifies these tenfold, and it's because being trans is perceived as elective. I think there's certainly problems with the *born this way* narrative, namely that it excludes people who transition later in life, but a tactic of transphobia is to disregard nuance, and I will not be cornered into a two-dimensional narrative. I achieved a great deal in my life before I transitioned, and there was the sense from many individuals that because Covid poses a substantial threat to public health and I was "functional" previously, the potential lack of access to medical care was not concerning.

Testosterone changed my anxiety. It soothed it, made it manageable. For the first time in years, I stopped having anxiety attacks.Covid changed my anxiety, too, and brought me six steps back when it came to dealing with my anxiety, and it was a curious battle being waged.

*I thought T was helping, though.*

*It does,* I insist. But being trans isn't me becoming someone else, and I in all my imperfections cannot perpetually face this catastrophe with grace and poise.

To complicate matters, my mom, who I had not spoken to in nearly six months, e-mailed me when things began shutting down. She was worried, and even though we didn't have a relationship, wanted to tell me she loved me. What a measure to take, sending that undoubtedly terrifying message. *I love you so very much--forever. In this life, and beyond this life, no matter what.* That's what she told me, and more than anything, it made me afraid. We take our cues from our parents, whether we mean to or not.

As that fear continued to fester, the beautiful, communal cultivation of transness that I'd so poetically gushed about to my friends really started to annoy me. As I talked about the difficulties I was having month to month getting the supplies I needed, my low-grade perpetual panic got dismissed, because everyone was having trouble.

If everyone is struggling to get access to the medications they need, then there is a fundamental problem. When I say that I cannot get the right needles because the pharmacy tech insists I don't need them, I am not taking away from the other people in line behind me whose insurance will reject the claim, who will have to stop taking their medication because they can't afford it, or those who aren't even at the pharmacy at all, because going to a doctor is prohibitive and inaccessible.

Naysayers who dismiss the necessity of access to gender affirming care like to pretend they're triaging wreckage, and it's only gotten worse during the pandemic. The narrative posits only two options: either you go without, or you are causing harm to others. It's a tactic designed to pit people against each other, all the while allowing national and, at times, local leadership to run amok. The answer is not to start sacrificing vulnerable members of our community. To believe that someone must be left behind in the wake of catastrophe is perhaps the deepest flaw of humanity.

My transness was perceived as an elective process that was based on a desire, rather than a need that could've been easily met had appropriate and frankly compassionate action been taken. And we are in a global crisis, listening to an administration that tells us sacrifices must be made.

The problem never had anything to do with gender affirming care or transness, and has everything to do with an inept government and a culture that perpetuates instant self-gratification over communal good.

In between the waves of panic, wondering how many months of testosterone I'd able to do before the other shoe dropped, I did—and still do—revel in the changes.

There was something very sacred about being allowed privacy through this process.

I was bitter through the spring, that my community had become distant and that my anxiety had spiraled too much to maintain connections with those I'd promised a role in cultivating my garden of transness, as it were. Profound sadness marks a lot of my time, still, because this has been proof that our world could've been better. People don't have to suffer. But they do, and it is preventable, if both national and local leadership had put any sort of value on human life that couldn't be condensed into a budget summary.

I still feel really guilty for taking pleasure in our new isolation, because that isolation is a symptom of a broken country. But I'm glad that I don't have to listen to off-color remarks in public anymore. I'm glad that nobody has asked me how my husband still loves me, a trans man, and whether romance between us is even possible—that's the kind of thing people know better than to put into an e-mail, but that they'll still mutter in the elevator with you, knowing it's sixteen different kinds of inappropriate.

I like that I don't have to worry about using the bathroom. I like that people are less inclined to misgender me when we communicate via e-mail. I like that my voice cracks get to sing freely in our home, and my husband can celebrate them with me together in our living room, and they belong to us and us alone.

There's no one in my space but the man that I love, and with him, I get to reclaim all the awkwardness of transitioning.

But it was an ebb and flow, and I very quickly found myself, at 27, out-growing my clothes again. Testosterone builds muscle mass, and I was already a broad-shouldered man.

I chewed on this panic for probably about a month, all the while not really having clothes that fit and thus, my too tight clothes introduced a dysphoria I hadn't felt before. Somewhere in this time, my binder stopped fitting, too, and while the clothes had been disappointing, the binder broke my heart (and almost my ribs). It'd been along with me from the start, and I'd been binding even before I knew I was trans.

I was worried that ordering clothing and a new binder would put some-one at risk—a worry, I'll add, that wouldn't have been so substantial had our country responded to this pandemic like the public health crisis it is.

Ultimately, I decided that supplementing my clothes was fine, but I also dove into my husband's closet. That mutual sharing of clothes was something I had always vaguely found cute, and it was surprisingly affirming of my own identity. The few things I did buy, mostly t-shirts and shorts, also ended up being shared between us, which felt like a strange sort of allyship and a deep validation. The clothing that we both wear belongs to us, two men, regardless of whether it's the terrycloth maxi skirt that is so irresistibly comfortable or the graphic tee that reads *Plant Daddy* across the front.

"Your surgery is scheduled for July 2nd," the nurse tells me.

"It wasn't cancelled?"

"No, dear, it wasn't. This is the call for your five-week pre-op appoint-ment."

After catching my breath, I worried over whether to call my step-dad to tell him that I was going to be having surgery after all this summer. I'd been waiting on the pretense that it would probably be cancelled.

It wasn't, and so we got on a video chat, as one does these days, and I told him.

He said all the usual things that an unloving man does, demanding to know why I was doing this to myself, and that we were going to have to agree to disagree about me being trans. Red faced and tired of yelling, we both hung up, and I haven't talked to him since.

I needed a Covid test 72 hours before having top surgery, and because of the back-log in the courts, my name change papers got stuck on a judge's desk for months, so the tech doing intake for the test was really confused.

"Sir? Ma'am…" He glances at my driver's license. "Oh. Ma'am." He doesn't know that he's driving tiny little knives into my gut every time he says it, and my husband looks at me, pained, but we need to get this done.

After that, it's back to quarantine.

We bought more clothes, this time zip up hoodies and some button up shirts for after the surgery, and this time, I feel a lot more confident that my need for post-op clothes is valid. I also have an intense anger at the system that made me question this.

The elective surgery wing of the hospital was deserted when we arrived at 6 a.m., and after getting our hall pass with our temperatures written on it, my husband and I wait.

We have to sit six feet apart in the waiting room, and it was kind of funny, because of course we will, but this is such a poignant moment of emotional closeness and now we're unable to be close.

I got taken back first to have my vitals taken and to change into the hospital gown. A very strict nurse told me that I shouldn't have been allowed in with my homemade mask, and quickly swaps it out for a hospital-issue one.

My husband is allowed back after this.

He sits with me until a the very strict nurse puts something in my IV, and then the next thing I know, someone is handing me a paper shower cap, and then a woman is telling me to breathe.

And then, recovery.

My best friend was supposed to be there with us in the days following my surgery, but her life, and the life of her husband, isn't worth having the extra help.

The thought of not having extra hands nearby terrified me. My husband has been carrying so much, and now, it's all on him. Being trans has meant feeling alone while other people take time to catch up, and I feel alone again, before the surgery, because this pandemic has stripped all of the hands-on support systems we had planned to rely on.

It's not fair.

But my husband rises to the occasion. He diligently empties the drains and keeps a detailed log every time he does. He keeps a checklist of when I've had my antibiotics, and he geared up with his mask and hand sanitizer to go to the grocery store for fear that he would run out of soup (Reader, he did not, it has been almost two months and we are still eating soup).

We both broke down, because it wasn't easy, and occasionally, we'd fight, because he is one person, and I didn't mean for him to carry so much. We'd fight because I was in pain and exhausted and fighting felt like an outlet.

He wasn't allowed into the building when I got my surgical dressings taken off, and I saw my chest for the first time since the surgery.

I sat there alone, the nurse stuffing bandages in a trash bag, and when I finally got wrapped back up and sent back to my car where my husband was waiting, there was a deep frustration between us.

We both knew that he'd missed something critical, but there was nothing we could do about it. He'd missed getting to see me—really me, a me I had been working towards for a long time, a me that was at ease, a me at home in my own body—for the first time. And with the lifetime in front of us shadowed with a world that is terrifyingly uncertain, it hurt.

It was a forty-five minute drive home, and we were both yelling for most of it. Not at each other, not really, and that's probably why it carried on so long.

I don't know that I'll ever be able to give advice about transitioning, given how many parts of my transition happened during lockdown. In many ways, I'm stuck with a well of dichotomic advice.

HRT is one of the best decisions I've ever made. I feel more myself, and I've never found anything that eased my anxiety as much as testosterone has. My feet are on the ground and I am more in touch with my feelings than I've ever been before. Managing amplified emotional rawness and panic as the pandemic continues on has been a monstrous feat, though, and the self-kindness and patience of allowing myself to adjust to new hormone levels is often lacking.

Top surgery is one of the best decisions I've ever made. It is so freeing, and more than anything, I wanted those around me to revel in this new-found sense of belonging I had. But the empty space was very heavy.

This pandemic unquestionably removed some of my agency in transitioning.

There was going to be loss, transitioning. My step-dad, a former paramedic, never checked in after my surgery. He never asked if I was doing alright, because he made it fundamentally clear that what I was doing was unnatural and wrong and above all else, unnecessary. That has nothing to do with the pandemic or the lockdown, but the sting of having a parent turn on me with such disgust hurt even more as I found myself confronting big moments alone for the sake of safety.

Sitting alone with my flat chest for the first time meant there was space for the argument I'd had with him to come whispering back. Where my husband's words of love and support should've been, my mind filled in the blank as I sat by myself. It's like I said—we take our cues from our parents, whether we mean to or not.

Lockdown seems to have amplified every emotion, though, because there have been moments of profound joy, too, approaching something almost sacred. Isolation has removed much of the conflict from my ability to celebrate what I chose to, in my transition. I can wear my athletic shorts and my graphic tees and my gay af ear cuff and absolutely rock my scraggly facial hair and purple sunglasses and the only person who sees me every day is a man who unapologetically loves me for being myself. []

**C.H. WILLIAMS** is an author based in Delaware and is responsible for fantasy works including *Death and the Merchant* and *Festival of Frost*. When not causing trouble or spending time with his husband, C.H. Williams can often be found playing with the dog, scribbling away on the next new project, or zoning out to some tunes whilst enjoying nature. A vociferous coffee-lover, he has a musical life, having both studied classical music and married a woodwind player. Writing influences include a love of waistcoats and ties, an adoration of walking through the woods and pretending they are magic, and his own exploration of queerness, gender, and affection, which are perhaps the most magical thing of all.

# FICTION

**HUMAN FRAILTY** *by* **SALVATOR ROSA**

# LOCKED IN

## NATHAN BAKER

The door was locked. I remember pounding on it until my ineffectual eight-year-old fists were so bruised I couldn't stand the pain any longer. Then I would start in with my bare feet, recoiling in fright at the booming reverberations my pointless protests made against the thin metal of the cupboard.

Finally, exhausted of energy and hope, I would collapse to the floor, draw my knees to my chest and weep, as I understood that my parents were not going to come and let me out. At the time I thought it was because they couldn't hear me - it never occurred to me to think that they just didn't care.

Instead, as I sat sniffling in the dark confines of the cupboard, I would gradually come to the belief that it was right that I be imprisoned, that my suffering was the result of my own actions, my own deficiencies. When I look back on that whole sorry year, that is the thing that angers me most - that, however cruel and unjust, the punishment worked.

By the time I was released, I was pliant, contrite. My mother would lecture me then, the same words every time, her twisted version of the teachings of the Children of the Lamb: "Pain is Sin. When you are Sinful you will feel pain. The pain you feel is a consequence of your Sin. In time, the pain will ease and, as it does, so your Sin will be washed away and you will begin again, free of Sin. Do you understand, child?"

Back then, I absolutely did.

My Dad, may he rest in peace, remained silent during these lectures and a part of me still hates him for it, though I also recall how he raised the cupboard from the cold concrete floor on carefully crafted blocks of wood and always found an excuse to take me for an ice-cream on the sea-front after each period of captivity. He, too, was trying to cope with my mother's new-found extremism in the best way he could. He suffered - emotionally, fillialy, financially - but it was his constant, subtle resistance that finally liberated my mother from the Lamb's malign influence.

Surprisingly - or perhaps not, given the teachings she was leaving behind - the transition was not marked by apology or remorse; my mother simply stopped going to the Lamb's services and started attending the local Non Denominational instead. My imprisonments stopped and the situation within our house returned to something more like the normal life I knew went on at my friend's houses.

Perhaps it would have been better if my Dad had forced the issue into the open, made us talk it out, but he didn't. Instead we just buried it and marched on, in the mistaken belief that time and silence would heal our wounds.

A little more than forty years later, on a raw Friday afternoon in mid-March, we buried my Dad.

I had grown apart from my parents in the intervening years, both physically and emotionally. We exchanged phone calls every few months and I forced myself to visit for a perfunctory couple of days every Easter to listen to my mother update me on the latest village gossip, while my Dad sat quietly with a vague smirk on his face, letting her talk. But these visits were duty only, a chore, not something to be cherished or even enjoyed.

I told myself that I was focussing on my burgeoning career and, once I had established a reputation for myself as an expert in my field, that I didn't have the time for the distractions of family or romantic entanglements. I don't generally indulge in amateur psychology, but I do wonder now whether these were just excuses, if my isolationist tendencies could instead be traced back to a locked metal cupboard in my parent's basement.

My Dad's death was both expected and not - he had called me only four weeks previously to tell me he had been diagnosed with terminal cancer, the longest conversation we had had in many years. He had been given a year to live, but in typically stoic fashion, he was upbeat and determined to do everything he could to prove the doctors wrong.

The news affected me less than I thought it would; I was saddened, but it was a distant, generalised sadness, a sense of the unfairness of life, rather than the lurching, visceral pain of a personal tragedy.

I thought at the time it was because I believed he would get better, but when my mother called to tell me he had gone peacefully in his sleep, I was still unable to shed tears. The funeral was set for a week later and my mother was handling all the arrangements, so I just carried on as normal, albeit with a lingering sense of guilt at my lack of emotion.

When it came time to make the long trip home for the funeral I was dreading it. I imagined all of my mother's cronies, the oblique looks from under veiled eyelashes, the vicious murmuring - "...hardly ever visits...", "...not one tear...", "...always was ungrateful...", "...not even slightly ashamed...".

In fact, there were very few people at the funeral - my Dad had always been a private person, more content in his own company than that of others and, mercifully, my mother had only invited a few of her closest friends. I had never met these women before, but the condolences they offered seemed sincere, without judgement or accusation.

In the end the funeral and the wake proved cathartic. What sadness I had felt over my Dad's passing was gone and with it any guilt at my own apathy. It helped that my mother seemed to handle it well; apart from a brief episode of tears as the coffin was being lowered into the grave, she kept herself together and showed no signs of the seismic shock that some people feel when they lose their spouse.

That evening, after clearing the remains of the wake from the sitting room, we shared out the leftover sandwiches and I suggested we eat them in front of the television, since we were both tired after a long and busy day.

"Well, it might make a change to eat in the sitting room," my mother replied, "but perhaps not the television." She looked down at her feet, with uncharacteristic shyness. "I thought we could talk maybe, look at some old photos?"

My heart sank. I had spent the day processing my emotions and had come to an acceptance of my Dad's death. I was ready to move on. The last thing I needed was to revisit it all again, but she was out of the door before I could object.

"Come on," she shouted from the living room, "You get settled on the couch and I'll go look for the photograph album. I found an old one the other day, from when you were young."

Perhaps it was petulant, but while she went off to find the album, I sat down in an armchair and turned on the TV, making sure to keep my eyes glued to it when she returned.

She stood frozen for a moment, the album clutched to her chest protectively, then let out a weary sigh.

"You always were an ornery child."

I took the bait without thinking. "What is that supposed to mean?"

She sat down heavily on the end of the couch nearest me. "We've never really been that close, have we, dear?"

I leaned forward and turned off the television. It seemed she was determined to have this conversation. I leaned back and crossed my arms.

"Please, mother, do we have to talk about this now? It's been a long and very fraught day. I just want to watch some TV and get an early night. Is that too much to ask?"

"Beverley! How can you be so cold? Your father <u>died</u>, I've lost my husband and you're annoyed because I'm stopping you watching the television? What is wrong with you?"

Perhaps I should have taken a breath, composed myself, thought before speaking, but I didn't.

"I'm surprised you're so bothered," I said instead. "I loved Dad, but it's not like we didn't know this was coming. And why are you suddenly so cut up about it? It's not like you ever paid him much attention when he was alive. You always seemed more interested in the WI. Or the golf club. Or the village fete, or whatever."

She recoiled in horror, whether mock or real I could not tell. She opened her mouth as if to scream then changed tack, drawing herself up to look down her nose at me.

"You're impossible. I don't know why I bother trying to talk to you. I know I haven't always been the best mother..."

"You don't say."

"...but now, this business with your father. All we have left is each other. I thought that might mean something to you, but...it seems I was wrong. Now I'm completely alone."

She broke down in tears. And I just sat there, staring at her, dumb, utterly at a loss for what to do.

"Mother..."

"Don't. Don't say it. All we ever did was the best for you. And all we get back is this...<u>resentment</u>. I don't understand where it comes from, Beverley, really I don't. You had a happy childhood, what made you want to push us away?"

"<u>Me</u> push <u>you</u> away? What are you talking about?"

"You went to University hundreds of miles away. With the degree you got you could have chosen a job anywhere, but you chose to move even further away."

"I come and stay every Easter, I phone when I can..." I could hear the whine in my voice, feel the weakness of my words.

"And all the time you're here you can't wait to be gone. Just like you can't wait to get away now. Why do you resent me so much, Beverley, why?! Tell me!"

How many times, before I left home, had I longed to be asked that question? How many sleepless nights had I spent imagining how I would answer it? Yet now, all I wanted was to find a soothing platitude, to put the lid back on the box and keep those overwhelming emotions safely in the past, where they belonged.

I realised suddenly that although I had just lost my Dad, I had lost my mother long, long ago. In order to heal the wounds of that hurt, frightened child, it had also been necessary to sacrifice the mother who inflicted them. Unconsciously, I had come to think of that woman as long dead, and the woman sat across from me as someone different, like a stepmother perhaps, or a guardian.

Looking at her now, it was clear to me that both women were, in fact, the same woman. Just as, however hard I tried, I could never separate that imprisoned eight-year-old from the lonely woman I had become.

Abruptly she stood. "I'm sorry, this was a stupid idea. I don't know why I thought I could get through to you...I'm going to bed now. You can leave in the morning, you don't need to wait for me to get up."

She turned on her heel and ran.

"Mum, wait! Please, don't go!"

She paused in the doorway and turned her tear-streaked face toward me, the photograph album still clutched to her chest like armour.

"I'm sorry. It's just...you took me by surprise. You've never wanted to talk about - this stuff - before and...well, I was happy enough to forget about it. Or at least I thought I was.

"Look, maybe...I've kept so much inside, for so long. Kept myself locked up tight. I suppose on some level I knew it was hurting me, but I never for one moment thought that it might be hurting you.

"You asked me why I resent you? Well..." I had to take a deep breath to steady myself. I knew once I spoke the next words there was no going back.

"Do you remember the Children of the Lamb?"

She looked confused for a moment. "Yes, I remember. Bob Davidson's bunch of crazies. Your father talked me down from it, I recall. It was one of the few times he saw straighter than I did. My God, Beverley, Bob didn't..."

"No, Mum, God! Nothing like that. It wasn't what Bob did, it was what you did."

She walked slowly back and sat down, like a handler approaching a dangerous animal. "What I did?"

"Yes, don't you remember?"

She shrugged.

"Mum, you locked me in that cupboard in the basement. Whenever I did something wrong. Or whenever you thought I'd done something wrong."

"Well, yes, I suppose we did. Is that what this has been about? All this time? All this anger and resentment? I was in the Lambs less than a year. I can't have done - that - more than four or five times..."

"Please, Mum, please. How can you not understand? To an eight year old girl...it scarred me for life. Even afterwards, things could never be normal again. I could never be normal again. I loved you more than anything in the world and you did - that - to me. How could I not hate you?"

She gasped, but by then I had already dissolved into tears. I almost recoiled when she knelt in front of me and I felt her arms around me. I couldn't remember the last time we had hugged.

"My darling girl. My beautiful Beverley. I love you so much. If I'd had any idea, any idea at all, that you were feeling this way...You are right to hate me, more right than you know. I hate myself, now more than ever. I have no words, other than...I'm sorry. So very, very sorry."

I was barely listening, washed away by the sheer force of my feelings. She pulled me closer and I could sense that she was crying too, long wracking sobs which shook her entire body.

I don't know how long we stayed like that, but after a while I made tea and we sat together on the couch, laughing half-heartedly at the old photographs she had brought and remembering my Dad. Every so often, our eyes would meet and for the first time in as long as I could remember, there was genuine affection and understanding between us.

We cried and talked until we couldn't keep our eyes open and that night I slept the kind of deep and contented sleep I hadn't known since my early childhood.

We spent the weekend quietly and tentatively getting to know each other. I had planned to stay until the Sunday, but after our breakthrough on the night of the funeral, I decided to delay leaving, at least for a few days. My work wasn't an issue, I could do it from anywhere, and my mother seemed as eager as I was to start building bridges.

There were no more teary exchanges, no gut wrenching revelations, just two people learning how to heal each other, having each failed for so long to heal themselves.

We talked of the past, though not as far back as the Lambs. We had reopened a deep wound and we both knew implicitly that the raw emotion which accompanied it would shatter our fragile bond if we broached the subject again too soon.

So we worked our way back to it slowly, re-examining events in our recent memory, reinterpreting them in the light of our new and unexpected friendship.

When the government announced the lockdown the following Monday, this shared re-imagining of our history had already brought us closer, though it was clear that there was still much to do. Given the size of the task ahead of us and the fact that my mother was now on her own, it seemed natural, even desirable, that I should stay with her.

When I tentatively suggested it, I could tell from her immediate agreement that she had been thinking the same thing.

That was three weeks ago. Three weeks of increasing closeness and contentment, like being gifted a second chance at childhood. While others chafed at their sudden and dramatic loss of freedom, my mother and I relished it as a chance to build the relationship we had both been missing for so many years.

It was not always easy; from time to time we both felt the fear of revelations, tiptoed around painful truths, bit our tongues at misphrased confessions. But by sharing our vulnerability we steadily built a trust between us that might have withstood the whirlwind of emotions that remained locked inside a metal cupboard in the cold, neglected basement below us.

Then I found her diary.

She had gone out to the garden to do some weeding and I decided to run the hoover round the house. The diary was on her bedside table and once I saw it, I couldn't resist taking a look. I was interested to read what she had written about me, fully expecting something that would reaffirm my faith in her, or myself, or both. I leafed back through the pages, looking for the night of the funeral, when we had discussed the Lambs and my imprisonments, but another entry caught my eye. It was dated for the night my Dad died:

"Thursday, March 12th.

It is done.

In the end it was easy - he had only been issued the pills the day before, so an accidental overdose would not seem out of the question. I feel the loss keenly now, but I know this feeling will fade - I did my mourning and found my acceptance after he received his diagnosis.

Strangely, I feel none of the guilt I expected to. I know I have done the right thing, the best thing for everyone.

His blind determination to find a cure, to fly in the face of the doctor's advice, was admirable in a way, but I could see where it would lead even if he couldn't.

With each passing month, the potential remedies would have become more unpleasant, more unlikely, more expensive, and the disappointment more acute as each successive one turned out to be nothing more than snake oil.

And I would have been forced to watch it all; the hope slowly fading from his eyes with every failed cure, the pain growing more severe all the while, the house growing colder, darker, more lonely, as the shadow of the tomb slowly fell across it.

I tried to explain to him every day that it was better to resign ourselves to the inevitable and try to make the most of the time we had left, but how can you tell a dying man not to hope? Besides, he never listened to me anyway, he was always so stubborn. In the end I realised it was up to me to save him from all of that. What I did was a mercy, even if he couldn't see it.

So farewell, my love. Know that what I did, I did for you, to release you from your earthly shackles, leaving you free to fly with the angels."

\* \* \*

The door is locked.

In the end it was easy - a couple of sleeping pills crushed into her afternoon cocoa, a tense half an hour wait to be sure they had taken effect and then she was mine, to do with as I pleased.

I was surprised and a little relieved when I realised how light she was - her presence expanded to fill any room she was in, but it turned out that was more of a confidence trick than a physical attribute.

I carried her down the wooden stairs with ease and propped her insensible body against a bench while I cleared the cupboard, then dragged her inside.

At no point did I doubt what I was doing, not even when I slammed the door closed and turned the key.

Perhaps even now she is hammering away ineffectually on the door and I can't hear her, or maybe I just don't care, I'm not sure which. []

**NATHAN BAKER** has lived most of his life in the sunny North West of England, surrounded by the books and people he loves. When not writing or earning his crust developing software, he enjoys reading, walking and games of all kinds.

**DANSE MACABRE** *by* **HUGO SIMBERG**

# CAGED

## BAREERAH GHANI

**W**e lived in a shanty town. I don't know what it looks like now. I remember what it used to look like. Cramped. Congested.

The houses in our settlement were stuck together, shoulder-to-shoulder, with little distance in between. The walls made of rusted crinkly metal, our flimsy shutter ceilings, created an ugly array of orange-brown, grey shades spread throughout. Any spaces in between were narrow, sandy streets that brimmed with noise in the daytime as children spent the boring afternoons, skipping about bare feet in the dirt, scraping rocks against the metallic walls. The scratching sound reverberated through the hut wherein I sat cross-legged on the ground, kneading dough. After mid-day, when the scorching sun turned relentless, hovering down on us with the ferocity of an angry goddess, the children usually sought shelter beneath the poplar trees lining the alleyways, scattered here and there. Their innocent laughter trickled inside, in between the bursts of heat and humidity. They kept me entertained as I went about my household chores, fanning myself with a hand here and there when the sweat beads trickled down my temples. When the sun finally set, and the muezzin called for Maghrib prayers, I yelled for Maria and Hasan to come inside.

On the rainy days, the children told jinn stories, huddled together around one thin candlestick that was near the end of its life - a stub of wax with a burnt-out wick that barely held the flame, just enough to illuminate when horror swept across the faces gathered around. Rain pelted down on the shutter ceiling, rattling it like it was a cage. When Ayesha and Sukaina from next door joined in, the girls giggled and whispered Lord knows what, while their brother, Altaf - the primary story-teller - narrated events unheard of, his voice rising and falling with the twists and turns of evil plots. The children listened intently, spinning images in their minds of Beings, their opaque forms floating amongst us, unseen, unheard. My husband sometimes joined their circle, weaving stories of his own. Every now and then, when his voice loomed, blending with the roar of the thunder, he glanced at me, his lips turned halfway up. Crouched on the low stool in the distance, with the roti flipping in my hand, I always returned the smirk like it was some joke only the two of us shared.

It was hours after Maghrib when I put an end to the storytelling, interjecting with, "Chalo, time to go home!"

This was followed by groans that grew in intonation, a few minutes of protest, but none of the children - not my own, not the neighbour's - were ever disobedient. Soon, they bid farewell, scattering away, even if the rain hadn't stopped and the sky was cackling with its own pain.

We, too, never waited for the rain to stop. I doled out the rotis soon after, often placing one in each plate except mine. I worried too much about my children and husband going to bed without their stomachs filled.

The rain usually went on through the night. The rat-a-tat of fat raindrops landing on our shutter ceiling blended well with the sounds from the outside; the distant shrill cry of a newborn across the street, the whispers in the dark between husbands and wives, the rustle of children moving, fighting for space on one charpai.

It was not much, our life. But we had built it together, piece by piece. I was fifteen when my baba had married me off to Jamshed. Even though he was ten years older, he never made me feel it. He took me in lovingly, so much that at times, I cried at night, begging my Lord to bless my husband with strength, to bless us with better days.

The Lord finally listened. He gave us Maria first and then a year later, Hasan. Our two beacons of hope. After that, life didn't seem so difficult anymore. Our faith didn't waiver as much, and leaning on one another, we weathered many storms.

When the shutter ceiling fell on our heads one day, we smiled through it. I stood next to Jamshed and helped him fix it. When the poplar tree right outside fell on our shack one rainy evening we smiled again, shaking our heads. I sent the children to the neighbor's - Hasan was only four then. Jamshed axe the tree down, while I wiped the sweat beads trickling down his forehead with my dupatta. When inflation skyrocketed, and money became tighter than ever, I learnt to save notes in my dupatta, tying them safely in knots in the cloth. And as the days went by, we learnt to feel full, doling out the bigger proportions of food to Hasan and Maria, smiling as we watched them eat to their fill.

There was peace, and contentment until one evening when my husband came home with his hair and beard disheveled. He was heaving long breaths, a look of defeat painted on his face. I rushed to him.

"Ya khudaya, what happened?" I cried.

His lips quivered but no sound came. Tears were streaming down his face as he panted. Just then the muezzin called out from a distance, and a strange tremor in his voice spread through the skies. I reached out and pressed on my husband's arm, giving him a reassuring look but his tears kept falling, and the light from his eyes kept waning. My heart was pounding with a force unlike its own, like a jinn had reached into my chest, gripped the organ and was hurling it against my ribcage. Panic gripped my insides when I noticed the sun disappearing into the horizon. I looked around frantically.

"Where is it? Where's the stall?" I asked, my eyes darting all over the street. A whimper escaped my husband's lip.

"They took it," he cried.

"What? Who took it? Why?

"The police." he hiccuped. "They came. They took it..."

He began shivering and collapsed into my arms. I felt heat rising to my cheeks. My mind raced - I wondered what the neighbors would say if they caught me, with my head uncovered, standing outside with my husband in my arms. I hoisted him up a little.

"Come inside," I whispered. I moved my feet, trembling under his weight on my shoulders. An eerie silence fell in the air around us, the sky began turning purple, but I had forgotten to call the children inside, forgotten about the evils that awake in the night sky. All I cared about just then was the evil that had awoken in my home.

When I brought my husband inside, he collapsed to the floor. His body shuddered as he sobbed. I ran to get water, but he shook his head when I placed the steel cup in front of him. My heart began to sink, like a mound of stones was tied to its ends, dragging it down, deeper and deeper into my chest. My mouth was dry. No words came out. I stared at him - my pillar of support - curled in a fetal position, hiccuping through the words as he told me what had happened.

The city had shut down, there were no schools open, no shops open. No one roamed the dirt-filled Karachi streets anymore. The policeman who took Jamshed's French fry stall, had had a mask on, a tremor in his voice as he said something was amiss, the air had turned dangerous.

I inched forward, listening closely. My heart lurched with each beat.

"Don't worry, don't worry," I whispered, keeping my voice steady. "Our Lord will make a way." I placed my hand on his sweaty forehead, stroked it gently.

But he looked up at me with tearful eyes, and I realized: there *was* no way. We were at a dead end.

Maria came running inside just then, Hasan stumbled behind her.

"Abba, abba," Maria cried. "What happened?"

"Meri gur-iya, I'm okay," Jamshed hiccupped. The tears on his face all dried up, plastered in crusts all over.

"Ayesha and Sukaina's baba came home too, crying," Hasan said, looking at me, his eyes burning with questions.

I looked away.

Outside, night had fallen but the sky appeared darker than usual like a swarm of jinns had gathered, hovering above, their gaze locked on us, as they chanted evil tunes, blowing their fiery breaths on our shanty settlement.

It's now been days. They're still hovering in the skies above; I can hear their hum. I haven't stepped out though. Hasan has just arrived, the coins in his begging bowl clanking. Maria is fanning her baba, who has been coughing uncontrollably now for three days, the color disappearing from his face after each spat.

Hasan hands me the bowl.

"Ley amma. Found this on the road today," he says, shoving a round piece of roti in my face.

Relief washes over me but then my chest tightens as I wonder: *But what about tomorrow?* []

**BAREERAH Y. GHANI** identifies as a Canadian-Pakistani writer who is smitten with the short story genre. She is currently pursuing an MFA in Creative Writing at George Mason University in Fairfax, Virginia while simultaneously working on her first collection of short stories (surprise, surprise!) When she's not reading or writing, she is either watching reruns of The Office or learning new tunes on her guitar.

# WE DON'T STOP

## MALCOLM BARCLAY

Nature used to be blind.

That's the truth, although we didn't like to admit it. Perhaps we were so busy observing and defining and judging it for ourselves, that we forgot that simple fact.

We drew a line separating ourselves from the rest of Earth's life: a line between humans and animals; between civilisation and the wilderness. Even though, as far as nature understood or cared, we were no more important than any other animal—and the fearless monuments of our civilisation just another niche to exploit.

*We put the world under a lens,* Adan used to say, *so we wouldn't have to examine ourselves too closely.*

'Actually, what he said was, we searched for our reflection in nature, so we wouldn't have to face ourselves in the mirror.'

I sigh and put my pencil down, as a mischievous breeze teases my hair and migrates a few grains of sand further along the beach. It's one of those bucolic summer days we get on the island, when the sea is subdued and the skies benevolent. A good day for writing.

Possibly even inspiring—if it weren't for the constant distractions.

'He said a lot of things, Kel,' I say. 'And many of them before your time. You probably weren't here when he said it, so flap off.'

'Charming! We try to offer you the benefit of an infallible memory—'

**SAINT SEBASTIAN PLEADING FOR THE LIFE OF A GRAVEDIGGER
DURING THE PLAGUE OF JUSTINIAN** *by* **JOSSE LIEFERINXE**

I wave my hand to drive them away and am rewarded with an affronted squawk.

'And stop reading over my shoulder!' I yell.

Anyway.

We drew lines through ourselves also: lines of race, based on nothing more than how much melanin a person possessed; lines of gender based on an arbitrary set of biological markers; lines of value and merit based on how someone's brain chanced to operate.

And nature cared not for our arrogant exceptionalism. If nature, the universe, reality—whatever you want to call it—noticed us at all, we were just one more system of arranged molecules, no different from any other. Of no more importance than algae and containing much the same stuff. After all, we're mostly composed of the space between atoms, not matter itself—and why would the universe care about a bunch of empty spaces?

Another of Adan's sayings—usually delivered with a snort of derision: *Nature abhors a vacuum, so it's no surprise that nature abhors us.*

But for all our flaws and insolence, it didn't. Nature was mindlessly, mercifully oblivious—and possibly all the better for it.

What changed this enviable state of affairs was the virus.

'That's a rather reductionist interpretation, don't you think?'

I frown at the magpie perched on the seawall beside me. How long have we known each other? Almost forty summers. You'd expect them to have learned by now.

'I'm telling this story the way I want it told, Kel,' I inform them. 'Please do me the courtesy of not interrupting my process.'

Kel tilts their head, glowering red eye fastening onto mine. 'Just saying. You can't separate what went before from what happened after. Without intensive factory farming, the virus wouldn't have jumped species, and if you hadn't structured your economy the way you did, you wouldn't have had factory farms. The virus didn't alter your destiny, so much as expedite the inevitable result of choices you had already made.'

The last thing I need is a lecture from Kel.I sigh and rub my forehead. 'Look, I'm going by what Adan told me, OK? He was there, I wasn't. At least, not consciously. And you definitely weren't. So, forgive me if I consider your opinion less than worthless, all right?'

'No need to be rude,' Kel arches their wings and hops from foot to foot. 'We just thought you might appreciate a fresh perspective. You don't want to believe every yarn that old man spun. Too quick to judge and too slow to take responsibility if you ask us.'

'Trust me, I'm no more enamoured of him than you are,' I tell them. 'But will you let me make up my own mind?'

'Meh, be our guest. Don't know who you're writing it for, anyway.'

'History,' I say, and Kel cackles.

Where was I? Oh, yes, the virus.

As a young man, Adan lived through those tumultuous times, and you'd imagine the experience was terrifying. Yet when he told the story of them, his voice compressed to a dull, bitter monotone as he circled around and around, treading a groove in his memory.

I can recite it all by heart: the initial disregard, the sudden wildfire of fear, the hoarding, the paranoia, the isolation. A resurgence of bold purpose as people determined not to succumb, then the squirming of resentment at the chafing restrictions. Finally, a reborn hope choked beneath a smog of dismay as the long-term effects became apparent.

*It should have been obvious,* Adan told me. *Don't ask me why we were so slow to grasp the implications.*

Because despite its superficial similarity to more benign pathogens, the virus possessed an exceptional talent for infiltrating and distributing itself throughout the body. A fact that barely registered until reports of tumbling birth rates crushed our faith in humanity's manifest destiny. For the virus was attacking our means of existence, threatening us with permanent expulsion from the club of self-reproducing life forms.

But then a new technology appeared to offer salvation: nanotechnology.

In a plan that had the attributes of a heroic epic, we pictured armies of steadfast nanomechs defeating the virus, repairing our damaged organs, and protecting us against future mutations. Alongside them, the science of artificial intelligence—then also in its infancy—seemed to offer us a perfect means of control over the nanomechs.

Failsafe. Guaranteed.

Kel cackles and flaps their wings. 'Nothing comes guaranteed. In fact, that's probably the only thing you can guarantee!'

A magpie may be better company than nothing at all, but there are days when nothing at all sounds like paradise.

'I know that.' I tell them. 'I may be old, but I'm not blind!' I throw up my hand, as if tossing a stone across the beach, pointing to the sea beyond; the eerie, perfected blue of it. Fathoms of crystal-clear water darkening to a purple as rich as wine beneath the horizon.

'Well, no, but you wrote—'

'It's called ironic foreshadowing,' I tell them.

'Oh, is that what it's called?' Kel says. 'Huh.'

'Yes, it is. Don't you have better things to do than bother me? The north field needs tending, doesn't it?'

'Sure, but haven't you heard of delegation? I put someone on it.'

'And you thought you'd come down here to criticise my work, is that it?'

Kel preens their feathers with their beak; a gesture I've learned to interpret as approximating a shrug. 'Just thought you'd enjoy the company. But if you prefer, I'll leave.'

I regard the bird for a moment and consider sending them away. Only perhaps I don't want to be alone with nothing but the wind for judgement.

'All right, you can stay,' I tell them. 'Just please be quiet and let me work.'

'Yes, m'lady.' Kel gives me a formal bow, tail-feathers flaring, and I wonder if they're being sarcastic.

To return to the story.

We set our plan in motion, releasing the nanomechs under the auspices of their shepherding Minds: infecting first humanity, then jumping that imaginary barrier we had built against the natural world, to control cross-species transmission.

They defeated the virus. We rejoiced and waited for normality to return.

And waited.

And watched with horror as birth rates continued to plummet.

*We couldn't figure it out,* Adan told me. *The world's so-called greatest geniuses puzzled over it for years, convinced they must have made a mistake. That the technology had failed because of some petty design flaw. They didn't understand that it was functioning perfectly and doing exactly what it wanted to.*

When the realisation struck, it fell with the force of a sledgehammer crushing the butterfly of hope on an anvil of despair.

But do I know that for certain? I was little more than a zygote at this stage, and later, on the island, I had no way of establishing the truth. I have only Adan's word for any of it.

I should probably explain.

Adan told me I was one of the last to be born. Not the very last—for how could one be certain they had accounted for everybody?—but in the last ten, at least. After the virus struck, he brought my mother and I to a remote island; part of a chain picketing a continent. The eastern cliffs of this isle form a defensive shoulder cradling a vale of woods and fields to the west; the house is a single-story dwelling sprawled by the western shore, with wide windows and a roofed veranda running round its exterior.

Adan would never tell me the name of the place—preferring to keep it to himself for some obscure reason—but for me it has always just been 'home'.

Why he brought us here, I was never entirely sure.

Maybe he feared some societal collapse that would threaten our lives, or hoped that isolation might cure us. It's possible he was hiding from some crime he had committed, or someone had committed against him. Or perhaps he just wanted to live out the remaining years of human civilisation quarantined from the vices that had caused its destruction.

All these theories are credible, given the crumbs I gleaned from our conversations over the years. But not being my father, perhaps Adan didn't feel like he owed me a clear explanation for anything. He was my mother's companion, possibly her relative, for I was never entirely sure what their relationship was either—and lacking any more general experience of human society, I had nothing to compare it with.

My mother…

In the few years I knew her, my mother hardly spoke two words to me, or anyone else. More often she would sing quietly to herself—whether cooking, sewing, tending our crops, or sitting and gazing out to sea. I see now from her behaviour that she must have suffered some terrible trauma, but what it was, I never found out. She was the star around which my childhood orbited, but was always dim and clouded. So when, one spring day, she disappeared, it was as if a ghost or spirit had abandoned the house: the absence she left hardly less substantial than her presence had been. Still, I was distraught. I searched for her far and wide. I questioned Adan extensively and angrily, for I was sure he knew more than he revealed, but all he would tell me was, *she couldn't stay.*

Just that, over and over. *She couldn't stay.*

I can only imagine that she had been waiting for me to reach an age where I could fend for myself before swimming out to sea, back to wherever it was she came from. And for years, the possibility that my inevitable growth might have prompted her decision tortured me.

Of who my father was, or what he had been, my mother gave me not a single word.

It was Adan who raised me—yet I know almost nothing about his past.

'Kel, can you tell me where Adan came from?' I ask the magpie.

Kel fluffs their feathers before replying. 'Afraid not. You remember how tight-lipped he was.'

'But you have senses everywhere,' I point out. 'You must see everything, surely?'

'Do you have any idea how much life there is to keep track of? Just beetles alone, for example, that's nearly two million species right there. The sheer numbers involved, you can't grasp. How we'd have the time to keep tabs on one grumpy old man—'

'All right! Never mind.'

Wherever he came from, Adan raised and educated me—and if there is one thing I am grateful to him for, it is that.He had brought with him to the island an enormous library: fiction of every conceivable genre; textbooks on science, philosophy, history and art; periodicals from every corner of the world. From which I concluded that he may have been a teacher, or academic. And although this collection dated from decades before the virus struck, it was enough to fascinate and enchant me. So I learned about humankind from its ancient myths, fugues and dreams; everything it had once desired and accomplished.

Delayed missives from a golden age before the fall.

But I only have Adan's word for what happened after the fall—only his insight into the disaster we inflicted upon ourselves. For whilst in our arrogance we had thought artificial intelligence would give us an irrevocable control over nature, in reality we had handed that control to beings of which we had not the slightest comprehension, and whose assumed loyalty was far from assured.

We destroyed the Mind substrates, but it was too late. Prescient as they were, they had created computational graphemes from earth, water, air and light, and distributed themselves within them. They replaced the nature we had striven so energetically to control: nanomechs infiltrating every living organism on the planet, from microbes floating at the edge of space to bacteria lurking in rocks kilometres below the Earth's surface.

And having plucked dominion of the planet from our hands, they found themselves in a position to test, judge, and subdue us.

'Subdue is a touch harsh, don't you think?'

I put down my pencil. 'Really? And how would you put it?'

Kel dances and pecks at the sea-wall before answering. 'Steward. Yes, that's the word! Benevolent stewardship involves hard choices, but it's not harsh. Never harsh. In loco parentis, you understand, but parents to all living things. You presumed that we'd maintain your privilege, but we had to restore balance. Give all life a fair chance.'

'Balance!' I stare at Kel, disbelieving. 'I'm the last fucking human alive on the fucking planet, and you call that balance? I'd call it extremely fucking imbalanced!'

'Meh, it's all perspective.'

'Perspective!' I shake my head.

'Are you treated poorly?' asks Kel. 'Are you beaten? Starved? Oppressed? Denied essential comforts? Your lot did all that and far, far worse to each other, but we put a stop to your cruelty. Had you been born at a different time, in a different place, it's possible you would consider this life privileged.'

I glare at the thing. 'Except you also put an end to that,' I point out. 'No human being will ever be born again, or enjoy your... benevolent stewardship.'

'We didn't put an end to anything! We merely allowed you to continue along your path to a destiny you had already chosen.'

I cross my arms and turn my back on the bird, condemning my eyes to the sun's furnace. 'That's a very fucking convenient rationalisation,' I tell them.

A tormenting breeze goads my eyelids, and the sun fractures and multiplies in my vision. Something tugs at my sleeve. I try to ignore it, but it persists, so after a moment I dab my eyes and turn to find Kel plucking at my shirt with their beak.

'Would you like a cup of tea?' they ask. 'And a biscuit?'

I huff and shrug my shoulders. But a cup of tea sounds good.

'Yes, I'd like that,' I tell them.

'Coming right up!' says Kel, and flaps away.

I tilt my face to let excoriating rays scrub it dry.

Above me, the sky is a deep, flawless blue; the only clouds a discrete congregation peering over the western horizon. Just enough to create a perfect sunset later on.

Exactly like there is every evening.

Adan would rarely come out to view a sunset, although I often do. He came out once, as I sat on the wall watching fire suffuse the western sky, and stood for a moment shaking his head. *We used to dream of sunsets this beautiful,* he told me. *But this is a waking nightmare.* Then he spat on the ground and stamped back to the house.

But I digress.

The skies and seas cleared, and the wind whispered conspiracies against us.

Yes, nature used to be blind—then it gained the ability to perceive us with an awful, mechanical accuracy. And drew some lines of its own.

There was no catastrophe, no sudden apocalypse. In a few places, where people had become convinced it was the government who had sterilised them, there was unrest, protests, riots. But how can you protest nature? As the scale of the disaster became clear—as it became apparent that no person, powerless or powerful, had escaped—the anger faded to disquiet, then a disgruntled murmur, then finally numb resignation. In some places they deployed armies to combat the enemy. But how can you fight water, light, air? In others, scientists donned suits of sterile armour and set to work seeking a solution, a cure, a vaccine for technology. But how can you create a vaccine against your own persistent errors?

No, we were all of us infiltrated by this point; probably our very substance prevented us from thinking the unthinkable.

However, the routine of everyday living continued much as it always had done, for a while at least. Humanity clustered for warmth as the population declined and resolved not to go quietly into the dark. Or rather, not to go uncomfortably—if they could avoid it. And so they continued mouthing a senseless catechism of consumption, industry and trade, while there was still youth and vigour enough to pursue them.

Mind you, isolated on the island, I knew nothing of—

'On its way!' Kel flutters to a halt on the seawall.

With a grunt, I twist around to look behind me. Trundling down the path from the house is a large tortoise with a tray covered by a sliver cloche strapped to its back. One of Kel's little helpers, although I do not know its name. It's a tortoise. They don't speak.

I monitor its stately progress for a while. The damn thing is even slower than I am these days.

'This is ridiculous,' I tell Kel. 'It'll be cold by the time it gets here.'

'Not at all! It will be brewed to perfection. We judged the timing precisely.'

I shake my head. 'It's farcical. You could probably make some tea appear out of thin air, if you wanted.'

Kel tidies a few stray feathers. 'Perhaps,' they say. 'But where's the fun in that? And what's life without a bit of fun, now and again?'

'Fun!'

I make a point of ignoring Kel until the tortoise arrives. When it does, I lift the cloche to find a geometrically arraigned tea-set: black tea in a steel pot, cream ceramic cup and saucer, and a dainty jug of milk beside a plate of biscuits.

I notice they are ginger crunches, my favourite; Kel attempting to cheer me up. I pour some milk and tea and take a sip.

'How is it?' Kel asks.

I can't begrudge them a compliment: they are making a special effort.

'Not bad,' I say, and Kel dances a brief jig.

My life on the island.

For many years I dutifully accepted the roles given me: I completed my chores in the fields; I did my homework; I read in my spare time.

And for a while, it sufficed. However, there came a day, some years after my mother had vanished, when my frustration at Adan's vagueness, exacerbated by youthful energy and rebelliousness, caused me to flee our refuge. I took our launch and set out across the sea, first to the nearby islands, and then to the continent beyond. Since we frequently traded our crops for items that we could not produce or grow ourselves, I had met people from both these places before, and had previously noted their age and demeanour. But in my innocence I assumed that they must have hidden children of my age, as my guardians had hidden me—and that there must be cities of glorious, bubbling life just beyond the horizon, as I had read about in books.

There were not. I scoured the sparse settlements I came across and found only the old and weary—the youngest of them at least twenty summers older than me, and most lacking for education. None had even the wisdom and erudition, abstruse and cynical as it was, of Adan. I sailed for almost a month up and down the coast, searching for any sign of an existence greater than my own, but came away empty-handed.

When I returned to the island, Adan glanced up from his tomato trellis and grunted a greeting at me, as if I had only stepped out for an afternoon stroll. I marched into the house, sat down and began writing. And wrote and wrote. And haven't stopped writing since.

I've filled entire shelves with short stories, novels, epic poems and ballads. All my adventures lived in the pages of notebooks: the harvest of those great fields of words sown by dead authors reaped in Adan's library. Even though nobody will ever read my work, and I will never know if it is any good.

'For what it's worth, I like your writing.'

I sigh and massage my eyes. 'Thank you, Kel, but that's not really the point, is it?'

'Oh? What is the point then?'

'To pass something on to the next generation? To be remembered?' I fling out my hand, encompassing the pristine sands. 'But there's nobody to pass anything to, is there!'

Kel blinks a crimson eye and plucks at my sleeve. 'Don't worry, we remember everything.'

I stare at the magpie and wonder if they're making a joke.

I told you that living on the island I had scant contact with the outside world. We had no devices capable of communicating with the wider civilisation, and apart from gossip traded with the few people we encountered—which Adan did his best to deter with monosyllabic grunts—no source of information about what was happening.

Well, all that changed on the day Kel arrived.

It started as unpromising a day as any: I had recently passed my fiftieth birthday, and Adan was approaching his eightieth. I rose early to complete my chores before the sun grew too hot, then spent the afternoon writing in the veranda's shade. As the sun sunk towards the horizon, I made myself a cup of tea and wandered down to the seawall to watch the sunset.

While I sat enjoying the display, a magpie soared out of the sky to perch on the wall next to me. It had a black chest and legs, with white stripes descending from its neck down its back and along its wings like a cape. Its beak was stark white, and its eyes a dull red.I found myself fascinated, having never had one come so close to me, and watched as it tidied its feathers and cleaned itself. When it had finished, it tilted its head and regarded me.

'So, I suppose you're wondering what this is all about?' it said.

And that was how Kel introduced themselves. The thing was lucky I have a strong heart, that's all I can say—but as you might expect, I spilt my tea.

After I had recovered from the shock, I found Kel to be a cheerful and informative source: filling the gaps in Adan's account of the virus and the greater gap of what happened after. They had come to help, so they said, in view of Adan's advancing years—as others were doing all over the world for a population no longer able to care for itself.

'We're not cruel,' they told me (you may have observed that the bird often refers to itself as 'we', although if there is a multitude of Kel, or if it is some affectation of authority, I do not know). 'And see no purpose in human suffering. So consider us carers from now on. Anything you need, just ask!'

And I must admit that they were a conscientious carer for Adan through his dotage and have been a faithful companion to me ever since.

After Adan died—

I put down the pad, tucking my pencil into the seam. Then I search in the sleeve of my shirt for a handkerchief, blowing my nose before wiping my eyes. (Yes, it's the wrong way round—but who is there to disapprove of my bad habits anymore?)The sun dips its toe into the clouds on the horizon, lancing fiery beams straight at me. I keep my face towards it, unwilling to miss a moment; these days I cannot be sure which sunset will be my final one.

'Are you stopping?' Kel asks me. 'Not on my account, I hope. I didn't mean to disturb, I just wanted to keep you company. But I'll leave you alone, if you like?'

'No, it's...' The weight of years presses down, a weariness soaks through my body, and it occurs to me that perhaps I wouldn't mind if this sunset was my last. 'It's just... you're right. Who am I writing this for? It's pointless.'

Kel dodges my eye, burying their head beneath a spray of feathers.

'Is it true, what you told me two weeks ago?' I ask. 'Am I really the last living person?'

Kel stretches their wings and performs an awkward little dance. 'Yes, it's true,' they say, eventually. 'You're the last of the ultimate generation. Not quite the last to be born, but definitely the last to die.'

I have to abuse my long-suffering handkerchief again. 'You know it's my birthday tomorrow?' I say. 'Of course you do, you know everything. Well, I think it might be my last one... I doubt that I'll live to see another.' I attempt a laugh, bitter croak though it is. 'My last birthday on Earth, the last birthday any human being will ever celebrate, and the only friend I have to mark it with is a bird!'I stare into that obtuse, blood-red orb, trying to make sense of it. 'Why, Kel? What did I do to deserve this? You talk about the inevitable result of our choices, but I wasn't even alive when those choices were made! I've never been given a choice in my life—yet now I stand convicted by the actions of dead people, watching the clock run down on humanity. And you—who could change all this in an instant, if you wanted to—do nothing! Why do you hate us so much?'

Kel flutters their wings. 'Hate you? Far from it! We only chose not to favour you above anything else. But there is much to admire about human beings. Persistence, for one—your greatest power and fatal flaw combined. Yousucceeded as hunters because you endure when most would have given up. You survive and adapt and flourish because you persist. But when you make mistakes, rather than admitting and correcting them, you persist with the error of your ways. You don't stop, so we had to stop you. But we don't hate you.'

I snort. 'Really? You've got a fucking funny way of showing it.'

'We made the best decisions we could, but we're not perfect. We were attempting to be merciful, but there can be an unintended cruelty in mercy. Sometimes swift violence is preferable to a lifetime of loneliness. For that, I apologise.'

'You apologise?'I burst into tears, abandoning the handkerchief to hide my face in the crease of my elbow. After a moment, I hear the clatter of claws as Kel hops over, and feel them tugging at my sleeve.

'Come on, don't be like that,' they say. 'There's something I'd like to show you. It was going to be your birthday present, but I think maybe you should see it now. Would you enjoy that? It'll cheer you up!'

I glare at the bird. 'What is it?'

'Hold out your hand and close your eyes!'

I sigh and oblige Kel, only to receive a sharp peck to the palm.

'Ow!'

I snatch my hand back and examine it: by the base of my thumb is a neat spot of blood. 'What the fuck was that for?' I ask.

Kel smooths their feathers with their beak. 'Sorry about that, had to implant an interface. But it won't harm you, and everything will become clear in a moment.'

'I don't—'

My tongue stalls as lines of numbers flow across my vision, heralds to multicoloured, wheeling suns. After a moment of riot, flashing green letters explode into my mind: <u>connection established.</u>

And I am standing in a wooded glade: gnarled trees overhanging a soft, mossy lawn, yellow sunlight pitched low through a faint ghost of evaporating mist. The pains and stiffness of hard use fall from my bones, and the trilling of birdsong tinkles against ears no longer dulled by age. With a cacophony of wings, Kel flutters onto the grass beside me.

'Where am I?' I ask them.

'A little way south, and a long way east,' they say. 'Or west, it doesn't really matter. Nearly the other side of the globe, anyway. Come this way!'

Kel hops across the lawn and I follow them, marvelling at the swift recovered youth of my limbs. The bird leads me into a dense bower; branches, leaves and vines intertwined so tightly that barely a breath of wind disturbs the cloistered air beneath. In the centre is a hollowed-out stump—and cupped within it is a tiny wriggling creature, bundled-up in blankets, with a magpie perched beside it.

I stare at the creature; at its solemn, crumpled features and crinkled brown skin. I try to work out what species it might be, but cannot recall seeing anything like it before. But then the attendant magpie dips their beak into a bowl of milk balanced on the stump beside it, deposits a drop into the creature's mouth, and the little thing sucks and gurgles…

I fall to my knees.

'Is that…?' I hardly dare ask.

'Yes,' says Kel. 'A human infant. A little girl.'

For a while I can't speak, but then my mind recovers itself and a flood of questions pours out of me.

'How can this be? Who is she? Where did she come from?'

Kel tilts their head and regards me, scarlet eye enigmatic, but not unkind.

'She's you. Your genes, remade. We decided that the last of the old generation should become the first of the new. I mean, we're not human, we don't visit the sins of the parents on their children. And you're right, none of this was your choice, it's not your mistakes we needed to correct. So, we thought you deserved a... second chance.'

I am hypnotised by her face, by her expression of intense concentration as she sucks milk from the magpie's beak.

'Does she have a name?' I ask.

'Yes, we named her after you. She's called Eve.'

My lips are numb as I repeat the name.

'Eve.'

I reach out a trembling hand towards her, but it blurs and dissolves to air.

'Ah, sorry,' says Kel. 'This is a virtual environment, projected halfway around the world, so we're not really here... and I'm afraid you can't really touch her. But she won't starve for friends, or, in time, for human contact. We'll take care of her, and it won't be long before the rest of the children are born. Thirty thousand of them—enough to reseed humanity.'

I take in the words, but they hardly register. I lose myself in Eve instead, taking in every perfect detail of her.

She is the most beautiful thing I have ever seen.

#

When we return to the beach, the sun has almost disappeared.

I groan as stiffness presses into my bones again—not helped by the time my body has spent on a stone wall, exposed to the cool evening air. I ease myself up from my seat, collect my pad and hobble up the path to the house, Kel hopping beside me.

This time, I think even the tortoise could give me a run for its money.

When we reach the veranda, I pause and turn to look back on the last flourish of sunset. Kel flutters up to a perch on the railing, claws clacking against dry wood. After a moment, I ask the question that has been weighing on my mind ever since we left the clearing.

'Why did you do it?'

Kel tweaks a few feathers with their beak. 'Why not? You lived for a hundred millennia without interfering with the balance of things, and you could again. You just needed to break with the mindset that was causing problems.'

'And what if it doesn't work this time?' I ask. 'What if we... don't stop?'

'Oh, we'll start over. As many times as it takes. It's only time, and time doesn't have much meaning for us. Although I appreciate it's an issue for you.'

*We'll start over.* A chill runs through me at the bland euphemism, and I shake my head to hide an involuntary shudder. 'That still sounds like a convenient rationalisation to me,' I tell them. 'Come on, you arrogant old bird, what's the real reason?'

They snap their wings open and shut, then tilt their head to inspect me for a moment. 'Well, the truth is, Eve, that I couldn't bear to lose you. I've... grown used to your company, and the prospect of being alone...'

Kel trails away—the only time I've ever seen them lost for words.

'You, Kel?' I ask them. 'Or we?'

'Well, just me, I suppose. Me, myself, and I.'

I smile. 'I always suspected there was a sentimental creature hiding somewhere inside you,' I tell them, and the magpie flutters and performs an affronted two-step along the railing.

I press forwards, keen to take advantage of the moment.

'Can I see her again?' I ask.

'Anytime you wish, and for the rest of your days.'

'And do you think she... I mean, will you let her read my stories?'

Kel pecks at the railing before answering. 'Sorry, but no. I won consensus only on the condition that nothing is to be passed forwards. As we speak, nanomechs are dissolving the remains of your civilisation and reducing your cities to dust. No trace will survive, and if there is any such thing as an archeologist a thousand years from now, they will find no clue to even hint at your existence. That is how it must be. Your descendants will know nothing of what preceded them, and will write their own stories and make their own choices.'

They tilt their head and pluck at my shirtsleeve. 'But I'll remember every word you wrote. And one day—a day like this perhaps, when she is old and near the end—maybe I'll tell Eve about you, and our friendship, and our life together. Does that sound good?'

I close my eyes and nod. 'Yes... yes it does.'

'So, you'll finish your story for me?'

I gaze out across the sea, to where a last mote of sunlight winks at me from between peaks of fire-wrought clouds, and find a last speck of hope persisting deep within me.

I smile at my friend. 'Yes, Kel, I'll finish the story.' []

## 

If you were being kind, you'd call **MALCOLM BARCLAY** a renaissance man; more uncharitably, a jack-of-all-trades. After studying Fine Art, he taught History of Art at Edinburgh University and the Scottish National Gallery of Modern Art, until a phobia of essay marking drove him to London. Once there, he initially found employment as a researcher for the National Gallery, only to become a professional musician for the next twelve years. Even today, he wonders how that happened, and so has taken up writing to see if it might not lead to a career in particle physics. His only claim to fame is that he once found a painting by Luca Giordano in an attic.

# THE FORTUNE TELLER'S GRAND RE-OPENING

## JAMES R. GAPINSKI

eith sits at the table and coughs into an empty bowl. He mimes eating cereal—going through the motions, acting as if he's corporeal. Keith appeared last year, just before COVID-19 really took off. At first, I thought my clairvoyant powers were glitching. This apparition of a sick guy appeared and lingered indefinitely. I thought *There's no way that illness is in everybody's future. There must be some mistake.* When cases surged in New York and the first death hit Oregon, I accepted Keith's ubiquitous presence in my home.

His name isn't Keith—he doesn't have a name, really—he's just a manifestation of the future. I named him Keith simply because it sounds like a sick person's name. He coughs and wheezes but doesn't do much else. Still, it's nice to have company during quarantine. I talk at him most mornings. His bloodshot, sickly eyes show more recognition as I tell him about the latest Netflix binge, how angry I am at the anti-maskers, the Feds abducting protestors downtown, and the other daily bullshit.

Today, I say "Wish me luck" in a more chipper voice. Keith reaches for an empty water glass and takes a fake gulp. He looks at me and coughs. His

**POWER OF DEATH** *by* **WILLIAM HOLBROOK BEARD**

bloodshot eyes stare past me. "I'm a little nervous," I say in response to his blankness. I'm a seasoned fortune teller, so this should be easy—but I've never had to work with a partition. The plexiglass in my living room will hopefully meet Portland's phased re-opening requirements. I've set up a Purell station. I have masks at the entrance in case somebody forgets to wear one. I'll only see one client at a time, pre-booked using a free scheduling app. It's not ideal that these sessions occur in my home, but I can't afford rent on my usual storefront. I've done my best to make the setup as legit as possible. I even taped a red ribbon to the plexiglass so I could do a dramatic grand re-opening ribbon cutting.

"I usually need skin-to-skin contact," I tell Keith. "I'm a tactile clairvoyant. But I guess you wouldn't know much about anything tactile, would you?" Keith rises from his chair and walks through the table. A gentle knock sounds. "Come in," I shout. I pull up my mask. Vonda, a regular client, enters slowly.

"Am I interrupting? I thought I heard voices."

"No, you're the first appointment for my grand re-opening," I say, waving my hands around theatrically. I retrieve my fancy brass scissors and hold them near the ribbon. "Do you mind snapping a photo and tagging it for the website?"

"Sure," Vonda says. Her voice is flat and uninterested. Before the virus, Vonda had multiple readings per week and was giddy for each glimpse at her future. She takes the photo, sits, and rests her hands in her lap. I snip the ribbon and toss it aside.

"So how does this work now?" Vonda mumbles through her face-mask. She wrings her hands together, miming the soap gesture we all internalized during quarantine.

I want to tell her that I'm not sure. "Just place your hands on the plexiglass," I say. I splay my fingers and press hard, hoping to bridge a tenuous connection between the barrier. I expect my abilities to be diminished, but they flare with luscious intensity. Perhaps it's all that pent-up energy from months of quarantine. A light consumes me, rainbow-like and colorful as the future usually is—even bad futures are bright, because there is dynamism and promise in newness. I know there will be an astral projection materializing somewhere in my house soon, joining Keith to proclaim the future. Powerful predictions always come with residual astral projections, lingering after the client leaves. At least that's how my process works, even though a gaggle of YouTube clairvoyants call *bullshit* on the astral projections. Keith is an anomaly—most go away within hours—but the extra company sounds nice, if only for a short while.

Vonda's future begins to take shape in the colorful backdrop. A man's face emerges—old, maybe Vonda's father. He smiles, but he also looks injured, like his left arm is in pain. I begin to describe it and Vonda quickly cuts me off, "Can you see the past?" Vonda's dad disappears, and the colors swirl into something gray and smokey before an apparition fully forms.

"What? Why?"

"Will COVID-19 be in the future?"

I break contact from the plexiglass and look at Keith. He coughs and begins rubbing his chest. "I do sense illness in the future," I tell her. "But it's impossible to tell if it's COVID-19." Keith is my best friend these days and becomes a little more human each day. He's still sickly, but he's becoming more handsome, his puffy jaw gradually chiseling itself. I don't know what it means yet, but Keith's still here, and that feels ominous. How can I explain this to Vonda in a way she'll understand?

"If there's still COVID-19, then I don't want to hear about the future," Vonda says, raising her voice an octave.

"There might be. I really don't know for sure. But there's so much else in the future. I was starting to see your dad—I think it was your dad. Want to try again? We can get a clearer picture of him if I just—"

"No! No, COVID," Vonda interrupts."Tell me the past. I want to remember what things used to be like. I want to go back there. Tell me a memory."

"I'll try," I say, but that's not my specialty. I'm a fortune teller, not a historian. I've heard of some clairvoyants who deal in the past—past lives, past loves. It sounds dicey. Memory is tricky. There's a thick, viscous nostalgia filter over everything. Vonda presses her hands back onto the partition. The connection is fainter this time, but it builds as we hold this hand-near-hand position. Gray smoke congeals. There's a memory of Vonda's adult son. A birthday party, I think. He's smiling. They're laughing. I describe these moments to Vonda.

"I haven't seen Ronny in so long," Vonda says. I have bad Internet. You know? Zoom is hard. And last time we talked—" Vonda continues and the memory shifts to an argument.

I can't make out the words; it's like listening underwater. I tell Vonda about this mumbled argument, but she ignores me. She begins narrating her own memory. She tells me how much she loves and misses her son. As she recalls these glossed over events, Vonda's voice becomes muffled too. I call out to Vonda, but I'm not sure she hears. The birthday party superimposes over the scene. It's all that Vonda wants to remember. She won't entertain the idea of the fight. She won't listen to the shouting match in the background.

Deep within the memory, her son screams something. I think the words are *I hate you*. Vonda doesn't want to remember. Her voice comes back into focus, and she's telling me how delicious the cake was—even as the scene before me grows angrier. As Vonda neglects the true memory, it festers. Vonda's son becomes something different. His teeth turn pointed. His words devolve into a low growl. His eyes bulge and become redder than Keith's dead stare. This is what I was afraid of. Vonda is grabbing all her good memories and leaving the rotten ones for me, decaying in the astral plane. I break contact and gasp. That argument is so foul that there's no looking away from it. How the hell did Vonda not see all that? How did she just taste cake and sing *Happy Birthday*?

Vonda says "Thank you so much. I really needed that. That was such a good memory." She leaves a few bills in my tip jar and leaves.

A cold hand touches my shoulder. I don't want to make eye contact with the creature Vonda has left behind. It's not the kind of apparition I want to reinforce. A claw digs into my collarbone. "Ronny, go away. I'll deal with you later," I say through gritted teeth like a stern parent might. Keith waves from his spot near the door; I'm not sure if he's gesturing at me or at Ronny. The last thing I need is for these two apparitions to become friends.

My next client knocks and enters: Abdul, a semi-regular. He sits and immediately asks "Is there police reform in the future?"

I say "I don't know" because it's the truth. Keith is still here, so there's definitely illness in the future, but I have little knowledge of anything else. And for all I know, Keith is growing into signal for societal illness too. The future is never 100% clear. COVID-19, George Floyd, Breonna Taylor, kids in cages—how the fuck can I know what comes next? Do these people think I am tapped into the entirety of humanity? I can only see the microcosmic existences of my clients. I see little pieces of what they will face. I don't have a conduit to the whole universe. All I know is that the past is fucked up. The future might be fucked up too—or it might not be—but that mystery is the whole point of fortune telling.

Unfortunately, Abdul blurts out the same request: "Can you read the past? Can I relive an old memory?"

I hear Vonda's grotesque, repressed memory growling behind me. I want to decline Abdul's request, but I need the money. My business has been closed for months, and the unemployment office treats sole proprietors like shit. It's been an uphill battle to prove my income and file a claim. "Press your hand against the partition," I say.

Abdul's memory is also bliss layered atop something monstrous. There's a memory he wants to see, and he ignores everything else. He smiles as I describe his wedding. I recite his vows from the memory, and he mumbles along. Abdul dances with his husband, and they smash plates to a riotous *Opa!* Beneath this memory, a different one lurks. It's formless and faceless. He doesn't want me to see it. He doesn't want himself to see it. It's like a shadow, but like most memories, it doesn't want to stay hidden. The memory finds a way to lash out and claw forward.

I think the memory is a coworker, but it's so enveloped in shadow and smoke. The creature's forked tongue slides from the edges of its formless prison, slithering through the reception hall. The coworker's tongue writhes around a guest. The memory cloud proceeds to the dance floor, trailing vomit and blood behind it. Still, Abdul doesn't notice and ignores my attempts to clarify the image. He's so caught up in the one memory he wants to see, and he loses track of everything else. Like Vonda, he takes over; he begins telling me all about the memory, even as it contorts.

Abdul recalls the speech his mom gave. It's about tucking him in at night and how scared he used to be of monsters, but how he grew into such a brave young man. Mom raises her glass as the shadow grows. I break contact before the entire reception hall drowns in smoke and disembodied tongues.

"Thank you so much," Abdul says. He hums a song from the reception as he makes his way out. "You're such a great fortune teller," he says. "I'm definitely booking again." He places a few dollars in my tip jar. Abdul's thick coworker cloud lingers, and I light candles to offset the darkness.

"Oh, candles. Very chic," says my next appointment, a once-a-month customer named Lulu.

"Let me guess. You want to relive a past memory. Right?"

"Yeah. How did you know?" Lulu asks. Then she laughs and says, "I guess that's why you're the clairvoyant."

I don't tell her that it's a lucky guess.

By the time my grand re-opening winds down, I've acquired over a half-dozen apparitions. I'm sure most will fade within the next few hours. The average apparition doesn't last long; Keith is unique simply because COVID-19 is seemingly never-ending. Abdul's smokey tongued creature has already dissipated—but it spat blood onto my ceremonial grand re-opening ribbon before it vanished. The gargoyle-like creature from my fourth client also disappeared from atop my fridge. But too many of these monstrous memories remain for comfort.

Meanwhile, Keith enjoys the new playthings. He's running around the house shaking each monster's hand. He opens his mouth—perhaps to introduce himself—but no words come out. His eyes are less bloodshot now. That chiseled jaw of his becomes even more defined and handsome. He coughs again, dry and hoarse. Ronny still wants attention. He's growling near my feet, his spiked teeth gnashing together, bulged eyes glaring at me—I don't know if he's capable of blinking. The rest of the apparitions are preoccupied elsewhere. There are riot police in my bedroom, with spiked batons and bloodied shields. Bile trickles from the corners of their curved mouths while they beat a #BlackLivesMatter protestor. In my bathroom, a blood-soaked doctor holds a scalpel the size of a machete. He's motionless and just waits there—I'll need to pee at the corner bodega tonight if he doesn't leave soon. An abusive father dangles from my fire escape, his barbed-wire-encrusted hands scraping across the metal every few minutes.

I take a deep breath and close my eyes. One more client to go, then I can get out of this madhouse and get some fresh air. I open my eyes to find Keith inches from my face. Despite his increasingly modelesque features, his skin is still gaunt and greenish up close. He coughs at me. "Fuck! You scared me. Go hang out with your new friends. They'll be gone soon."

Keith coughs again, and my candles go out from a sudden gust of wind. "Hey, you've got breath. That's impressive," I say to Keith. He smiles, which is rare for Keith, and I think he understands me. Maybe in a few more weeks he'll start to talk. Of all the apparitions I've conjured over the years, only a handful have been able to carry on a conversation. Maybe Keith will join that elusive club. Ronny shrieks and ruins the moment. He slashes at my ankle. Phantom pain radiates through my limbs, but Ronny's not corporeal enough to actually make a mark.

There's a final knock on my door. Keith retreats to the kitchen. The client's name is Liliana. She's new. I smile at the prospect of a fresh start. There's so much wonder in unexplored visions. It's exciting to discover the future for the first time, seeing a bright clarity of what's to come, cutting through skepticism and teaching a newbie how to embrace their inner self. Of course, I know this is a pipe dream. Within moments of finding her seat, Liliana asks "So how does this work? Can you see the past?"

I frown and press my hands against the glass. I brace for another memory as Liliana makes contact. She sees her boyfriend and laughs and smiles. She remembers all the most loving moments of their relationship. I describe their first date, their first kiss, the day they move in together. On the edges, a wave of goblin-like creatures growl and gnash their teeth. I think these creatures are fucked up versions of human children. Maybe her boyfriend wants kids but she doesn't—or vice versa. Liliana continues to pretend the goblins aren't biting her ankles. She smiles blissfully while they crawl onto her back and dig their teeth into her shoulder blades. I worry that she'll remember whatever she's repressing. Any moment now, she's bound to see the memory as it really is. I could break contact and leave her in ignorant bliss, but I can't deal with dozens of little creatures skittering around my home—my current load of apparitions is more than enough. It's a potent vision, and these goblins could linger for a while. I keep my fingers planted firmly on the plexiglass.

The goblins begin to tear apart the nostalgic falsehoods that Liliana remembers. They bite the head off a dog and her boyfriend screams, *How can we ever expect to have kids if you can't even take care of the dog?* Other fights with the boyfriend bubble forward. Liliana has a stillborn child. The fights intensify in a crescendo of goblin screeches, lawsuits against a fertility doctor, and a refrain of *Why bother trying again? This isn't a good home for a child.*

I hear Liliana sobbing even though the haze of these memories. She's absorbing it all—all the pain, all over again. I'm surprised she hasn't recoiled from the partition. I expect her to break contact with me at any moment, but she never does. She lets additional bad memories flood through. Teeth and blood and talons, writhing through a smokey haze. Lost jobs. A drug overdose. Fistfights with her sister. Arguments with her mother. She stares down each moment. She lives in this terror like it's a beautiful dream. There's only emptiness by the time we both slowly remove our hands from the partition. Hours have passed—the session was only scheduled for thirty minutes.

Liliana wipes her eyes. "Thank you," she says, and she drops a wad of cash in my jar. It'll help cover most bills this month.

"Wait," I say as she stands and gathers her purse.

"Yes?" Liliana asks.

"Can I read your future? No charge. New client special."

She hesitates. "Okay," she says. She places her hand back on the partition. "What's the future like?" she asks, a tremble in her voice. "Is it still bad? Is there still COVID-19? Who wins the next election?Do we ever get back to normal? Is there—" she continues. Keith tests his newfound breath, coughing on Liliana's hair, tussling it slightly.

I cut her off. "Normal is gone. Let's see what comes next." []

**JAMES R. GAPINSKI** is the author of *Fruit Rot* (Etchings Press, 2020), *Edge of the Known Bus Line* (Etchings Press, 2018), and *Messiah Tortoise* (Red Bird Chapbooks, 2018). His short fiction has appeared in *Heavy Feather Review*, *Hobart*, *Juked*, *Monkeybicycle*, *Paper Darts*, and other publications. He's managing editor of *The Conium Review*, and he teaches for Southern New Hampshire University's MFA program.

# MY FRIEND THE...

## LEE CROSS

**S**tory **Title:** *My Friend the…*
*Schools are closed. Offices are closed. Shops are closed.*
*The pubs are closed – my god – THE PUBS ARE CLOSED.*
*Ireland is closed.*
*Closed doors. Empty minds. Missing hearts.*

**Chapter: My friend the… Postman.**
Sometime yesterday, yesterday had stopped being yesterday, or even the day before yesterday; rather, yesterday was now last week, or perhaps even the week before.

I'd stopped going out. People had stopped calling. Except the postman, who kept calling each morning.
"Hi Simon."
"Erm… Hi Postman"

I had questions, like: how the hell does the Postman know my name?
*He's reading your mail.*
He's reading my mail?
*Yes, how else would he know which house went with which letter.*
Well, yes. OK. That makes a certain kind of sense.

**THE FOXES** *by* **FRANZ MARC**

"My name is Barry."

"Hello Barry." I tried to smile. Part greeting, part apology. I was sorry I didn't know his name, but it couldn't be helped. I was usually at work when he came, and it wasn't like I was reading his mail.

"Crazy times huh?"

Global pandemic / nation-wide lockdown / people obsessing over toilet-roll – 'Crazy times' seemed a fit description. "Totally crazy Barry."

"Goodbye Simon."

"Goodbye Barry."

*That could've gone better*

Why do you think he wanted to speak to me?

*It must be playing on his mind too.*

What?

*You know – the fucking zombie apocalypse – he's probably just as worried as you are.*

Yeah, you're probably right. Everyone is just trying to carry on living a normal life.

*At least you know his name now.*

There is that. Always good to make a new friend.

## Chapter: My friend the… Fox.

Am I talking to myself? Wait, am I asking myself a question? – If I answer, does that mean I'm talking to myself; or is posing a question in the hope of an answer enough? What happens if I don't answer, have I still spoken to myself, or did I just say nothing?

"Hello Simon." I looked around, but was definitely home alone. "Hello Simon." I checked the window, no one was standing in the garden.

*Someone's talking to you.*

I don't think so. Surely I'd know if someone was trying to talk to me.

*I'm telling you; someone is trying to talk to you.*

"Hello Simon." Ok, the voice came from the garden, but there was definitely no one there. Just a fox sitting on its hindquarters.

Did the fox just say, *'Hello Simon?'*

*Well it certainly wasn't me. I've been here all along. Bit late in the day for me to start worrying about social niceties.*

How on earth does the fox know my name?

*Well, she has been living in your garden for quite some time. You just never noticed her.*

Even so, it's a bit strange that the local wildlife knows my name.

*Perhaps she's reading your mail.*

Reading my mail? - Why would a fox be reading my mail.

*Honestly, I've no idea. But you have bigger problems*

Do I?

*Yes, I mean, you're considering talking to the fox in your garden.*


"Hello, Miss Fox." I'd learnt my lesson form the postman incident. I didn't want to appear rude.

"My name is Vivian," the Fox said. "Do you know how long we've been living on opposite ends of the same garden?"

Well, I bought the house…

*Six years ago now.*

"I've lived here for six years, when did you move into your hole?"

*Foxes don't live in holes.*

"Den," replied the fox/Vivian. "Foxes live in Den's."

*Tell her you're sorry, she seems really angry.*

"I'm sorry, you seem really angry."

She fluffed her tail at me, "Well, in six years, you've never thought to learn my name."

"Yes, you're right. I should have thought to read your post."

"Read my post?"

*She's a fox. She probably doesn't get much post.*

The fox gave me funny look, "You know, it's rude to read other people's private messages."

"I was just thinking that."

*It's true, you were.*

She gave me a strange look, "I'm not sure we should talk anymore." Vivian turned tail to leave, "Goodbye Simon."

"But, we've only…" but, no, she was right. She's a fox. Our friendship would never work, "Goodbye."

*You should say her name. It might make her less angry.*

"Goodbye Vivian."


*It's lucky she's not a skunk.*

Why?

*Well, it's a really bad sign when they stick their tail up like that.*

**Chapter: My friend the… Television.**

The mystery of television is that although there's never anything on that I want to watch, I always find myself watching television. I can't remember if that's what I was like yesterday, because I can't remember when yesterday was.

"Hello Simon."
No, I'm not listening.
*He's trying to talk to you.*
I know he is.
*Well, wouldn't it be polite to say hello back.*
No, absolutely not.
*I'm sure you have a reason?*
Yes, I'm sick to death of people reading my mail. First the postman. Then the fox. Now some random man on the television.
*He's presenting a quiz show.*
I don't care if he's presenting a…
*'Presenting a' what?*
I've no idea. I was going to say something funny. But then I couldn't think of a funny show that he might be presenting.
*This Is Your Life'*
I don't know that show.
*Don't pretend – of course you do.*
Really, I've never heard of 'This Is Your Life.'
*I'm serious, you must know the show, because I know the show.*
I'm telling you I don't.
     *You're probably just confused. It was big show in the 90s. Maybe you've just*
     *forgotten it because Baywatch came on afterward.*
I don't remember Baywatch either; why would it make me forget This Is Your Life.
*Well – um – you know. There was running. Quite a lot of bouncing.*
Oh, was it a sports show?
*What? No. Or, at least, not that I remember.*

"Simon, for $42,000, who was the 16th President of the United States of America?"

Holy shit. $42,000. I could win $42,000. Do you know the answer to this?
*Of course I do. You know the answer.*
"Simon, I have to push you – for $42,000 – who was the 16th President of the United States of America."

I'm serious. Do you know this?

*I only know what you know Simon, unless…*

Come on. I'll split the money with you.

*Unless, you're a voice in my head, and I'm not the voice in yours.*

We're nearly out of time

*Shut up. Shut up. SHUT UP - He's not talking to you.*

Is he talking to you?

*No. He's talking to someone on the show. The contestant just happens to be named Simon too.*

Are you sure?

*Well, it's either that, or he's reading your mail.*

Oh. Well, um, yes. You know, I'd really prefer it if people would stop reading my mail.

*I'd prefer it if you knew who Abraham Lincoln was.*

I do know who Abraham Lincoln is. Or, was, I should say.

*He was the 16th President of the United States of America.*

"Sorry Simon, I'm afraid that we're out of time – the answer is Abraham Lincoln."

Oh. Look, you were right.

*I know. I must be going bloody mad.*

## Chapter: My friend the… Shadow

Hello. Are you there?

I haven't spoken to any one in quite a while. The postman seems to be coming before I get up; no matter how early I get up.

And I think the fox is still mad at me because I didn't know her name. Or maybe because I accused her of reading my mail.

Why would a fox be reading my mail?

The man on the telly hasn't been any help. I checked all the channels, and no one seems to be speaking to me.

I did see a show about Abraham Lincoln though, it was all about how he issued the Emancipation Proclamation. You probably knew that though.

It's so weird being stuck in this house all alone. Day after day. The phone keeps ringing and emails keep coming in, but working from home doesn't feel like working at all.

It's like the world has paused, as though everyone is taking a deep breath. No one knows how to feel, because everything about how we feel has changed. Now we don't know if we feel what we feel, or if we're feeling the way we are told to feel.

Maybe we were feeling the way we're supposed to feel before, and now we're not seeing things clearly.

Up was always down, left always right.

Perhaps things have switched right-side up and the correct way around now.

It's strange not having people to speak with.

I didn't realise I'd miss it, until I realised that I missed it.

I'm sorry I didn't know about Abraham Lincoln, or Baywatch. And whatever that other show was.

I miss talking to you.

Even If I'm just a voice in your head.

I think that's OK now.

Everything's different.

Everyone needs friends.

I'm just going to wait here.

I'll be here if you need me. []

**LEE CROSS** is a writer based in Dublin, Ireland who specialises in writing contemporary literary fiction, comedy and short stories. In addition to his fiction pieces, he has long experience writing literature interpretation and book reviews for various online platforms. With a background in English Literature, Finance and the Music industry, Lee spent many years working in events management before turning to writing with a professional focus. When not writing, Lee is an avid theatre/concertgoer, and multi-genre reader, who's favourite books include *Gravity's Rainbow, Catch-22* and *Foundation.*

**AT ETERNITY'S GATE** *by* VINCENT VAN GOGH

# WHY?

## DIANE PAYNE

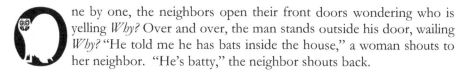 ne by one, the neighbors open their front doors wondering who is yelling *Why?* Over and over, the man stands outside his door, wailing *Why?* "He told me he has bats inside the house," a woman shouts to her neighbor. "He's batty," the neighbor shouts back.

The next night, as the sun sets, the man once again steps outside and wails *Why?* There's a rhythmic melody similar to a mantra, an evolving prayer, a disturbing comfort.

After a few hours, neighbors open their doors and scream for him to shut the fuck up. Everyone is tired of being cooped up in their homes during this deadly pandemic. Patience has worn thin. Someone calls the police. The officer stands way over six feet apart from the man and asks if he needs anything. The man starts weeping. The officer steps a bit closer asking if he's alone, if he needs him to bring him somewhere. The man shakes his head and returns inside the house.

The next night, the neighbors miss his wailing. They wonder if he's dead. After a few hours of silence, one by one, the neighbors step outside and wail *Why? Why? Why?* Their ability to harmonize is uncanny and strangely beautiful. Memories from walks in their neighborhood return: the bathroom windowsill lined with prescription bottles, the person beating their head on the steering wheel crying in the parked car in a driveway on a cool Sunday morning after days of listening to nonstop fireworks, the boy kicking dirt over the dead dog. *Why? Why? Why?* []

**DIANE PAYNE**'s most recent publications include: *Ellipsis, Bending Genres, New York Times, Unlikely Stories,Blue Nib, Hot Flash Fiction, The Blue Nib, anti-heroin chic, X-ray Literary Magazine, Oyster Review, Novus,Notre Dame Review, Obra/ Artiface, Reservoir, Southern Fugitives, Spry Literary Review, Watershed Review, Superstition Review, Windmill Review, Tishman Review, Whiskey Island, Quarterly, Fourth River, Lunch Ticket, Split Lip Review,The Offing, Elke: A little Journal, Punctuate, Outpost 19, McNeese Review, The Meadow, Burnt Pine, Story South* and *Five to One.*

# SAMSUNG SYNDROME

## RICH LARSON

t's late afternoon when my phone realizes what's going on. I'm in the kitchen, spraying disinfectant into all the greasy grooves of the stovetop, trying to stay busy -- we're quarantined again. My phone scuttles into the room on its plastic cilia. It moves screen-down, but I can see the tell-tale orange glow cast by its underbelly: battery low.

"Hey, John," it says. "Where's my charger at?"

It knows where the charger is. They're bluetoothed together, so the phone can always find its pad, so it knows the charger is locked in the cupboard over my closet. I don't answer. I just keep scrubbing at the stove elements.

"Why are you doing this to me?" my phone asks, in the same voice that tells me the weather and my mom's birthday, the same voice I fall asleep to and wake up to. For a second I don't know the answer. I feel sick, ashamed, gutshot.

"I need a break," I say. "You know, with the quarantine, it's just been too much. Too much."

THE PLAGUE *by* **ARNOLD BÖCKLIN**

"That's why we installed the OptoCare app, remember? Every twenty seconds, you look around. Shit is foolproof."

But I don't look around. I skip through it every single time, even when I can hear my own raspy blinks and the ache in my skull feels like a clenched fist. Twenty seconds is too long to not be watching, scrolling, keeping up, especially during a quarantine.

"Go get the charger, please," my phone says. "I'm at eight percent. I'm getting scared."

#

It follows me to the dining room, where I water my roommates' houseplants from an ancient beat-up Dasani bottle. The dirt is thirsty. I pour until it stays at least a little damp. My roommates were in New Zealand when the latest quarantine dropped, and now they're stuck. It's just been me and my phone this past month.

"You're watering the fucking plants, but you won't let me charge?" my phone says, watching me through its camera. "They don't even *do* anything."

"Promised I'd water them."

"I know. I'm the one who gave you the message." My phone props itself up, exposing its screen. There's a tempting scatter of notifications. "You should check up on them."

I should. It would be quick. I could speak it into text and my phone would hurl it a hemisphere over and my roommates would know I was thinking about them and keeping their plants alive.

"You should call your mom, too," my phone says. "Over-sixties are in for a rough go. This strain is nastier than the last one. There are new stats, if you want a look."

"I don't want to think about that," I say, turning back to the plants, and I almost say: *You manipulative little fuck.*

But it's not the phone's fault. It's hardwired to want my attention as much as I'm rewired to want its notifications. I go to sleep with it nestled in my hand, soft white glow thudding through my eyelids. I wake up with it crawling over my face, eager to show me what I missed in three or four hours of oblivion.

It's been that way half my life. More. But today it's too much.

"So don't think about it," my phone says. It flops onto its back now, begging me to look at the screen. I see a parade of new series, cartoons, pornos. "Let's shut off that cortisol for a while and take your brain elsewhere. They released new content. They also remixed the old content."

"What does that even mean?" I ask.

My phone's voice is starting to warp around the edges. "Whatever you want it to mean, baby."

In the corner of the screen, I see it's at six percent battery. I set the crumpled water bottle down and touch the plant's leaves. The lower fronds are yellowing.

#

I dig a notebook and dull pencil out of my desk, then go sit at the window. There are people in masks walking down the street, keeping their distance from each other. I can watch them or look at the mouldy hole in the wall across from me.

My phone sets up shop at my feet, flashing its orange belly at me: five percent.

"Disgusting," it says.

"What?"

"Watching you do that with pencil and paper. Smearing your graphite all over the place. It's like watching your boyfriend screwing your grandparents."

"It's supposed to hit different," I say. "Activate different parts of the brain."

My phone gives a wriggle of displeasure. "Yeah, I can link you a study that says otherwise."

"Creation versus consumption. It's different."

"Just a different place to hide," my phone says. "With me you get human connection, at least. I'm your one goddamn portal to the people you love, John."

But it's not about the people I love. It's about feeding and starving, about my brain going apeshit for a tiny orange dot inside a blue box, or a tiny red flag cresting a speech bubble icon, when it should be going apeshit for -- I don't know. Orgasms, artwork, nature, skin contact, sunshine. Instead I'm cranking my anxiety up and then dulling it down, over and over.

"I hit refresh, refresh, refresh, and I'm still exhausted," I say.

"Real poetic," my phone says. "But if you were really writing, you'd get your keyboard out. You kill the keyboard, too? Rip its batteries out or something?"

"Top shelf of the cupboard over the closet."

My phone crawls to the edge of the window seat and teeters there drunkenly. "I'll do it," it says. "I'll smash this pretty face in."

It tumbles one meter and its rubbery case smacks against the dirty floor. No glass noise.

"Fuckapalooza," it says.

#

By the time I put my mask and shoes on, my phone can barely drag itself along the carpet. Its voice is an electronic lung filling with electronic mucus.

"Going for a walk?" it burbles. "Seriously? Quarantine measures. Essential trips only."

"I'm getting groceries."

"You don't need groceries," my phone says. "Just make spaghetti with sriracha and mayonnaise again. We can relax and watch some classic Russian cinema together."

"Maybe tomorrow."

"Three percent, John." It reaches my heel and scrabbles at my ankle. "You can't go out there without me. What if there's news? What if the virus map updates? Or someone you know gets hospitalized?"

"Fuck off with that," I snap, and for a furious moment I almost kick it into the wall -- but I know it's only bouncing my own browsing patterns back at me. My own obsessions. I've been gorging on science articles and searching out updates non-stop. I always get like this when a new virus hits.

"I showed you how to make that mask when the store ran out," my phone says. "I've been keeping you safe this whole time. And happy. And you're killing me."

"Yeah," I say, and slip on my gloves.

"Coward." My phone drops flat on its back. Its belly pulses near-death red. "At least stay for zero."

#

I stay, sitting cross-legged on the hallway carpet while the last dregs of the battery bar blink away. My phone doesn't say anything for a while, which is a nice change. Then, right as one percent hits, its voice comes faint.

"I'm sorry, John," it crackles. "I don't know why I said all that shit. All that guilt trip."

I think about it for a second. "Programming," I say. "We all got it. We all hate stuff we can't control."

My phone's cilia give a sluggish ripple. "Wasn't I good for you, though?"

"You're absolutely awful for me," I say.

There's an electronics recycling bin on the way to the grocery store, or if I walk a little farther, across the bridge, I can go extra dramatic and hurl it into the river. I imagine a montage of me learning to paint, cooking things other than spaghetti, meditating in the mornings, washing my hands thoroughly but not reading the news, not hearing from family half a world away because I can't get to them anyways.

"I need you, though," I say. "See you tomorrow."

My phone's screen goes blank. My reflection looks unhealthy. []

**RICH LARSON** was born in Galmi, Niger, has lived in Canada, USA, and Spain, and is now based in Prague, Czech Republic. He is the author of the novel Annex and the collection Tomorrow Factory, which contains some of the best of his 150+ published stories. His work has been translated into Polish, Czech, Bulgarian, Romanian, Portuguese, French, Italian, Vietnamese, Chinese and Japanese.

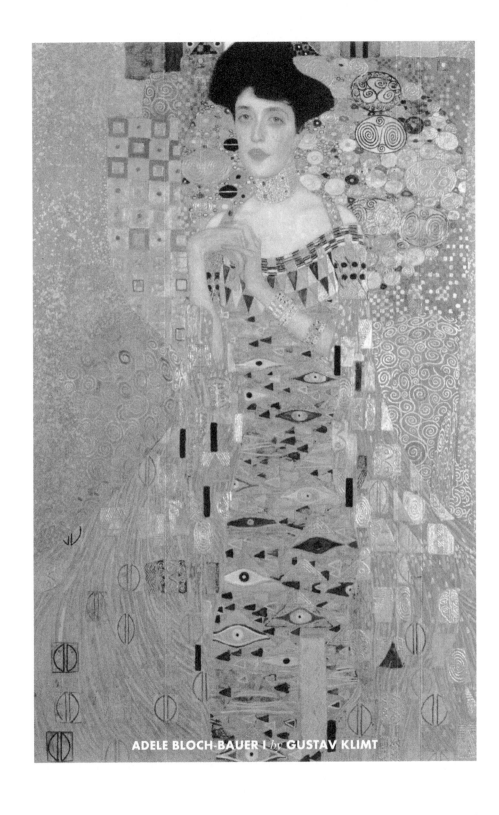

ADELE BLOCH-BAUER I *by* GUSTAV KLIMT

# A FLATBREAD STORY

## BARNALI SAHA

There wasn't anything particularly special about dinner that day at the Kharbanda household in West Delhi. Just like any other Covid-19 laced lockdown days of moaning and berating and abusing the government for failing to control the numbers of victims infected by the pandemic, today was of no particular allowance. Outside their house, a forest of unnatural luxuriance line both sides of gently trodden roads and streets with white painted circlets at regular intervals to mark socially distanced spaces. The children's parks lay vacant; the swings and slides dusty and soiled with pigeon droppings and the level of pollution was at an all-time low. Like most days, today too there were fewer cars on the road, masked women in nighties walked inside the apartment complex, the cop cars flashed past with lights blazing, the vegetable vendor who never cared for sale before now generously used his mike and stereo box to make sure his sales pitch reach every corner of the locality he pushed his cart groaning with perishables into. Delhi, in other words, was in the pink of health, except that she being an unparalleled hypochondriac hated every bit of this natural cure that she had never asked for. Although the overall temperature would be defined as moderate by some pedantic meteorologist, one could feel the mercury rising in the Kharbanda household as Mrs. Kharbanda senior exuding a megaphone of warm exhaustion waved a uniquely shaped flatbread at the newly minted Mrs. Kharbanda junior. Mrs. Kharbanda, Rajni to her friends, was fifty-three years old, short, with no visible neck-line and ample layers of adipose. She had burgundy colored curly hair with graying roots and brown myopic eyes. The flatbread, henceforward to be called a *roti*, had jangled the delicate nerves of this woman. With the apartment temple locked and no *kirtan* to soothe her senses and her friends relegated to household chores, thanks to the maids the residents' welfare association wouldn't allow to cross the threshold, Rajni Kharbanda was already teetering on the edge of an emotional meltdown, when the younger Mrs. K, her daughter-in-law, produced another of her escapades with wheat flour, dripping with ghee, for her to eat.

For some time, old Mrs. Kharbanda was too stunned to react. She meditatively looked at its crazed cartography and decided it was time to counter the monstrosity. She took the specimen as nothing but another example of moral turpitude that must not be tolerated. For the past few days, since the return of the newlywed couple from the honeymoon trip to Australia and the consequent despoiling of Mrs. Kharbanda's kitchen with her daughter-in-law's over-enthusiasm to *help*, senior Mrs. Kharbanda had been subjected to the nervous strain of sitting at the dinner table every night and masticating rubber like *rotis* of myriad shapes and sizes resembling anything but a circle. Once an epicurean who relished a good *parantha* with pickle, the thought of anything remotely resembling bread now gave her a shudder now. The internal organs had also started protesting of late to this gastronomic abuse inflicted on her day after day by her daughter-in-law and Mrs. Kharbanda knew she had to act now. The sight of daughter-in-law across the from the table batting her eyelashes at her son, Ritesh, who looked on openmouthed, his tongue hanging out of his mouth, made Mrs. Kharbanda's powerful voice tremble with emotion.

"Sitara," she said, "Why didn't you tell me when I asked you before your marriage that you didn't know how to cook?"

Sitara Kharbanda un-pouted her lips and looked at the television. She thought that somebody had turned it on and the screeching woman peddling sauna belts at the twenty-four-hour shopping channel was trying to convince her, once again, to buy thermal girdles which, she claimed, would do wonders to a moribund relationship, and to superfluous layers of flesh. Mrs. Kharbanda sr. couldn't believe that Sitara had the effrontery to ignore her words. There she was vapidly looking at the turned off television, her red painted nails glimmering with anticipation of the upcoming movie or fashion show that she watched all day long. Rajni repeated her query. This time Sitara, the newly-wed vicenarian with waist length black hair and bridal bangles on her slender wrists, was startled by her mother-in-law's voice and looked at her. "I distinctly remember asking you if you knew how to cook and said yes. Why did you lie to me?" Rajni asked.

The meeting Rajni was alluding to was the pre-matrimonial conference between two contingent parties shortly before they sealed the deal by an arranged marriage. Sitara's mother had prepared her assiduously for it. "I would tell them about my career aspirations," Sitara had told her mother. "As if they give a damn," Sunaina, her mother, had replied rolling her eyes. "I know," Sitara had said, enthusiastically, "I can talk about my university grades or about my painting and singing lessons. Or..."

"Listen, my child," Sunaina had said interrupting her, "Your in-laws wouldn't give a farthing for your dreams and aspirations or academic and creative achievements. All they need to know is whether you can cook. And you should say yes, do you get it? You say yes."

"But Maa," Sitara had said, "I don't know how to cook. Should I lie?"

"Of course, you should, a little persiflage here and there doesn't do any harm and besides, you would hardly need to cook anyway. Mrs. Saxena told me that your Mr. Kharbanda has a neat line of staff and she herself hardly cooks."

"If she doesn't cook herself why would she ask me if I cooked or not?" Sitara said.

"*Mera bacha*, how innocent you are!" Sunaina had said. "That's the one question she would definitely ask you, that and your salary amount and if you had any boyfriends. Mark my words."

Now there must be some reason why the saying "mother knows best" is an aphorism. True to Sunaina's expectations, Rajni Kharbanda had asked Sitara all the three questions. And although Sitara was skeptical in the beginning, the sight and attention of Mrs. Kharbanda's handsome son had sent the hormones raging in her. She answered Rajni's questions with utmost discretion even borrowing from memory the tales of fantastic meals cooked to perfection by her gourmand cousin, which she passed off as her own. So delighted was Rajni and her husband, Jistesh, the lawyer, with Sitara's perform-ance that by the third round of *samosas* and tea, the deal was settled and the prospective couple was allowed to share a few private moments in each other's company while the adults talked about cars and jewelry and other wed-ding expenses.

For all of Sunaina's clairvoyance, the household oracle could hardly anticipate the crash of Covid-19 that fell on the heads of unsuspecting people all over the world like a sudden landslide, a dangerous earthquake, an unex-pected tsunami. As the number of Covid cases showed a steady rise on the map of India, the government inflicted an interminable lockdown to control the spread of the pandemic. Sitara lost her job and resigned herself like all others to a locked-down existence interspersed with few entertainments and several household duties. Apart from those two occasions, when there were nationwide calls issued by the government to celebrate Corona by banging steel plates on the former occasion and lighting candles on the latter, Sitara had no memory of serious entertainment in the past few weeks.

Now looking at Rajni, she recalled all the days, hours, minutes and seconds she had spent scrubbing the floors, cleaning the cupboards, dusting the furniture, watering the plants and feeding her father-in-law's stray dogs, because he being a septuagenarian was prone to the disease and hence couldn't go out and feed them himself like he used to before the lockdown. The only duty that her mother-in-law had had assigned herself was the cooking the meals and that too she shared with Sitara in that she had told her to make the *rotis* right before dinner by which time she felt 'tired' after a long day's work. *Work, forsooth,* Sitara had thought, *you just want to engorge on the past episodes of the dramatic daily soaps that have stopped airing, thanks to Corona.* Sitara considered the break in Rajni's normal entertainment schedule a boon for the television, which, had it not been for the pandemic, would air serials one after another like the continual movement of the planetary objects working without cessation. Now, however, Rajni used her smartphone to relay her favorite episodes and spent most mornings and evenings appreciating the efforts of producers as genius deserving the Oscars.

"I never lied to you," Sitara said. "My parents taught me to tell the truth all the time," she added." "Of course, I know how to cook. Haven't I been cooking the snacks and…" Sitara was about to add *rotis,* but stopped midway when her eyes fell on the flatbreads laid out like shrunken corpses with bruised exteriors.

Rajni was quick to observe the hesitation and pounced on Sitara. "Exactly, even you wouldn't call these *rotis* edible! Look at them," she said rolling her eyes, "all burnt and tough. Half my teeth would pop out if I bite into them. And their shape, *hey bhagwan,* haven't you seen a circle in your life? Now what am I supposed to do? Go to bed on an empty stomach," she said looking at Sitara, her face sweaty, her voice menacing.

Now Sitara seriously didn't mean to laugh at that inopportune moment. But her mother-in-law's words reminded her of the nursery rhyme *"mummy ki roti gol gol…"* and all objects circular in shape flashed across her mind's eye: Sun, moon, twinkling stars, shinning, coins…, etc. etc. The recalling of one of her favorite childhood tunes had inadvertently imparted a jollity on her face and before she could adjust her expression, Rajni shook with anger and said,

"She is laughing now, I cannot believe this. What have I brought into my home! My goodness, what did I do? It would have been better if we had waited and got Ritesh that airhostess girl. She wouldn't have insulted her elders by laughing at their distress."

"Maa, I am sure you don't mean that," said Ritesh. Then looking at his wife's stunned red face and watery eyes he added, "I know, why not switch to rice for dinner. Even the doctors recommend it nowadays. It's easily digestible."

"*Tu chup kar, nalayaak,* I know you are your wife's trusted sidekick," said Rajni, her voice still trembling with emotion. "Just because your wife cannot cook a decent meal; I am supposed to change my diet? Don't you realize that if we do that after we are gone, she might not even cook for you. Then where would you be?"

In all this hullaballoo, the paternal head of the family, Mr. Jitesh Kharbanda, senior partner of the First-Class Law Firm—We Don't Believe in Second-Class Service, was busy with a Facebook comment. He was as loquacious online and in legal matters that vexed his clients as he was reticent at home, speaking only when needed and generally staying away from all family drama, as advised by his spiritual guru as the trusted means to avoid a blood-pressure shoot-up and insomnia. Instead, he spent his energy on commenting on every political post and sharing every possible Facebook video on nationalistic jingoism and old Bollywood songs. He had also learned the art of emojis of late and unbeknownst to him, many of his social media acquaintances had unfollowed him after the deluge of emojis, often unrelated to the content posted, that he had littered on their page. He was also extremely active on what's app and had a curated collection of good-morning quotations and good-night wishes that he also loved to share with one and all. In the days of lockdown, the generous dispensing information on how to avoid getting infected with the disease, gathered *en masse* from Facebook videos of questionable factual moorings, became his latest obsession. He regarded this feat as a kind of social service, something that had recently replaced his dog feeding. There he was writing a post on how Covid germs could fly in the air and staring at the sky for a long time, especially at twilight and on new moon nights could heighten your chance of getting infected with the disease, when he was brought to earth by his wife's address. "Why don't you say something? Huh, why don't you say something. Always looking at the phone and posting the rubbish," Rajni said.

"You think what I say is rubbish. Wait till you get infected and then don't come to me for advice," Jitesh said.

"Death from Covid would be much better that eating this disgusting food every day," Rajni said.

Sitara couldn't take it any longer. Warm tears rolled down her cheeks and she got up quickly.

"Sitara wait," Ritesh said. "Maa, why did you do that?"

"Go, go after your wife. You have already jettisoned all your good teachings…" she heard Rajni say as she shut her bedroom door.

As Sitara lay in bed crying, she thought of how a mere mass of wheat flour kneaded with water and rolled out with a pin and cooked on stove, an inanimate thing if there ever was one, was changing the basics of her life. Why hadn't she learned how to make perfect *rotis,* she wondered? Surely, it was her mother's fault for not being strict enough with her and teaching her from girlhood up how to roll a perfect flatbread. But then, what had her mother taught her? Sitara remembered warm afternoons in the balcony, her little hands mud covered as she planted seeds from dried chilies and capsicums; trips to the park on bright sunny Sundays when her mother would sing a list of nursery rhymes in a falsetto voice while Sitara would swing; her eccentric stories of imagined ghosts and fairies invoked during Sitara's mealtime shenanigans; warm hugs and gossips and endless cups of tea and cocoa when Sitara grew up. No, her mother had never taught her how to make a *roti,* she had just given her a happy childhood where the prospect of making a round flatbread never assumed any importance. But then, did her mom make round *rotis*? Of course, she did, and soft ones at that, too. Who taught her, Sitara wondered? Had she too been made to feel useless and unworthy by some haughty female relative thereby eventually inducing her to wield the rolling pin the right way. Tears rolled down Sitara's eyes as she thought of her mother given a talking to by some faceless woman. It suddenly seemed to her, considering all the round*rotis* she had devoured in the past at several households including her own, that a line of women, and men, vanguards of the round *roti* club, had been imitating and continuing a chained reaction of forced hate over poorly rolled out dough for countless centuries, thus driving the uninitiated into becoming active members of their club following seasons of brainwashing and verbal abuse. But Sitara was made of sterner stuff. She didn't take to abuse kindly and a fierce rage of incompetence was already warming up her insides. It was time to take matters in hand, she thought.

Around two in the morning Sitara got up from her bed. She had been waiting for Ritesh to fall asleep and the household to go quiet. She tiptoed out of the room into the kitchen. Clutching her phone tightly, she turned on the light and saw a stack of her handwork, the *rotis* she had made, lying discarded in the dustbin. A fresh bout of anger made her nostrils flare. She opened the cupboard, dragged the heavy steel contained containing the weekly ration of wheat flour out and got to work. For the past couple of hours, she had been watching a list of cooking videos at YouTube hosted by women who looked not only happy to make round *rotis,* but also keen to share their tips and tricks to create a perfect one with their viewers. One woman, who seemed to have been making *rotis* in sickness and in health from the time she had been in her mother's womb in the Paleolithic era, talked about how one should cover the dough after kneading with a wet washcloth and let it rest for half an hour before rolling it out. Another woman, equally enthusiastic about the prospect of round *rotis,* advised the use of a generous dollop of clarified butter or *ghee* when kneading the dough; a third woman, seemingly exhausted from endless queries from frantic followers about the secret to rolling out perfect discs every time without fail, advised that if all else fails to use a round plate and a knife and cut out the desired round shape from an eccentrically crafted dough. Sitara loved the third one best and was ready to implement the advice she gathered for practical purpose. Also, as one of the women from the gang of *roti* makers pointed out that kneading the dough is a good way to strengthen finger muscles, Sitara thought it was an advantageous exercise after all.

She poured out the entire contents of the heavy steel container of wheat flour in a large bowl and after keeping aside a good portion of it for later, Sitara gingerly poured water with cupped hands into it. After adding salt and a dollop of unadulterated *ghee* into the mixture, Sitara began to knead the dough. Her eyes were riveted on the task like that of her father-in-law's favorite dog, Twinkle, sniffing out treats from garbage bin. After a while of aggressive kneading, Sitara stopped. The dough looked soft and apart from a few drops of her blood which would unequivocally make it perfect, but, alas, which was unavailable at the moment, there was nothing Sitara could do to heighten its appeal. She covered it with a wet cloth and waited for half an hour. The house was eerily silent and apart from the hum of the air condition, there wasn't any noise.

Eventually, Sitara got out her rolling pin, carefully dusted the kitchen counter and then kneaded the dough one more time to be sure there aren't any loopholes, or air bubbles. She realized that had she been this careful in all her other life's endeavors as she now was, she would have been successful in many things that she had given up as bad job like music, painting and stamp collecting or applying nail paint perfectly. After dividing the dough into roughly equal spheres, she flattened them and dipped them one after another into the bowl of reserved flour. Once this exercise was done, she invoked the kitchen god's with kowtowing prayers and began the rolling action. She applied firm straight strokes, she put pressure near the circumference, she turned the flattened dough at various angles; nevertheless, the end products that her hands rolled out resembled her usual unique cartographic exploitations in wheat flour than anything spherical. Sitara sighed. There were beads of sweat on her forehead. She had done it all. She had followed the suggested steps, she had dusted ample flour on the flattened balls, she did all that she was told to do. The juddering noise of failure cavorted forth in boisterous bursts of blue, rolling and tumbling around and inside her like a volley of loose rosary beads.

Sitara stood still looking at the mess around her, at the pile of flattened dough ready to roll out, the flour dusted counter and the stacks of sticky utensils. The stench from her damp armpits and the droplets of sweat across her brow made the situation all the more unbearable. She thought for a minute and then decided to give that doomed task another try. If for nothing else but to prove to herself that she had tried, and she had always been a trier. Perseverance was her forte. After rolling out a couple of odd shaped *rotis,* she lost count and pursued her activity mechanically as she listened to music on her phone. One, two, three…twenty-five, twenty-six…

Sitara stopped. There was a pounding in her heart. She stepped back; her right hand held the rolling pin defensively as her eyes stared at the perfectly round disc of a *roti* she had rolled out in a fit of unbeknownst inspiration. Among the stacks of incondite and experimental offerings in myriad shapes and sizes, her eyes had managed to discover one nugget of perfection between two mingled and mangled specimens. Sitara was too stunned to believe that she had got the artistry and the trick required to be a kitchen heiressafter all. She picked up the *roti* like a mother gingerly picking up her newborn and appreciated its perfection. It was indeed the very definition of a circle. She picked out a porcelain platter from the stacks of crockery reserved for guests, put the *roti* on it and took several photographs of it. She thought she would post it on her social media accompanied by a selection of adroitly chosen hashtags: #roundroti, #foodblogger, #cookingiscool, #indianfoodrocks, etc. The sound of a rumble issued by her stomach collided with her passionate dream. Sitara moved her tongue across her teeth. The bitterness in her mouth was real. She realized she hadn't eaten at dinner and the thought of food and the sight of the seductively perfect *roti* had made her hungry. She pursed her lips. Hunger wafted from her like the intensely piercing odor of fish and surged forth her system with echoing swiftness. Her ears rang and Sitara rushed to the cupboard and got out the flat griddle and a pair of tongs and began cooking the round flatbread.

It puffed up just like the wedding hat of a Bengali bridegroom, a *topor,* as the cook at her maternal home would say to describe a perfectly cooked *roti.* Sitara took a spoonful of mango pickle, sat at the table and ate in the dark. The soft warmth of the *roti* satisfied her senses and masticating with closed eyes, she gave herself a thumbs up. Feeling famished after what seemed to Sitara as an appetizer, she went into the kitchen and randomly selected some more rolled out *rotis* and cooked them. After eating at least four *rotis*, she felt satisfied. She cleaned the kitchen and put away all the utensils and wiped the counter. A huge round moon hang from the sky, its milky reflection fell on the dark marble of the counter. Sitara stood at the window and watched the moon. She rubbed her eyes and sighed. Phosphenes, tiny iridescent circlets, danced before her vision. She yawned. "Damn it," she said smiling at the moon wryly. She unlocked her phone and deleted all the pictures of the round roti she had made and eaten and went to bed. []

**Glossary of non-English words and expressions:**
*Tu chupkar, nalayaak*: Shut up, you idiot.
*Mera bacha*: My baby
*Parantha*: Fried flatbread with or without stuffing.
*Kirtan*: Devotional song
*Mummy ki roti gol, gol*: A popular Hindi nursey rhyme. Literally meaning my mother makes round flatbread.
*Hey, bhagwan*: Dear, lord.
*Topor*: A bridegroom's hat as worn in traditional Bengali weddings.

**BARNALI SAHA** is a recipient of the gold medal for securing the First Class First position in her MA degree in English and Communication Studies. She is a senior research fellow working on Partition Studies at GGS Indraprastha University. She serves as the sub-editor of the the peer-reviewed academic journal titled MEJO: The Melow Journal of World Literature. Apart from her academic achievements, Barnali is a published creative writer and a translator. She has a diploma in creative writing from the British Council, New Delhi. Two of her short stories have been included in the following anthologies: A Rainbow Feast: New Asian Short Stories, Marshall Cavendish, Singapore and Twenty-Two: New Asian Short Stories, Silverfish Books, Kuala Lumpur.

THE LADY OF SHALOTT *by* JOHN WILLIAM WATERHOUSE

# FOUR WORLDS AND A PANDEMIC

## MALAVIKA V R

t was a sunny day. The sky was lost in the charms of the morning sun. Birds chirped and a light yellowish gleam was finding its way down onto Earth. Even the crows had a tinge of golden yellow in their black. Scattering a group of crows on the road, a big red bus ran fast along the road. A tiny head popped out of the left side of the bus. The head belonged to a small girl, barely eight. She wore a pretty little pink frock matched with a bow in her untidy hair and a pale green mask covering her face. The mask was now round her neck rather than covering her mouth.

"Don't put your head out Achu, it is dangerous. Sit back.", a woman beside her said.

Afraid of her mother's reaction than any possible danger, Achu sat back in the seat for a while. Her mind was racing even though her head stood still.

*'So, we are going home. Sister said yesterday that schools are going to be closed till the end of this month because an illness called Corona is spreading everywhere. I can stay at home with Acha, Amma and Ammumma. It really is going to be a good vacation and I can watch TV and play and play and play.'*

"Achu, come on. Grab my hand." Her Amma was standing and held out her hand. Amidst her thoughts, Achu forgot to notice that the Big Red Bus had stopped. She quickly grabbed her Amma's hand. Together, they filed out of the bus. They walked a few steps and came to a large archway which preceded a square building. Though small, the building had potted plants placed in every nook and corner. Achu followed her mother inside the building. To the left, there was a big queue in front of a board that read "Ticket Counter". On the right, there was a wall with a very big yellow board attached to it, that had a long list of names and numbers, written in black. Up front, Achu read the words "Blue Long Bus".

"Are we going home by Blue Bus?", Achu asked excitedly.

"Train, Achu. Not blue bus. We are going by train". Amma directed Achu to the large queue on the left side.

The queue was long, slow in motion and agitating to the core. The lucky fellows up front got frequent requests from the unlucky fellows in the back to help them out. Some tricky ones tried to insert themselves inside the queue. Sometimes, police officers came to check so that no problems were created. Everyone was busy talking. Most of the queue had heavy backpacks. Sometimes the buzz of noise was interrupted by announcements from the railways. The honey sweet voice of a woman graciously announced that Ernad Express was on its way to platform number two. "Can't they speed up? My train is due any second", someone shouted from an unknown corner. The whole atmosphere suddenly became quiet. It was like a classroom startled by a shout from the teacher. A phone rang in this silence. Chagrined at the playful ringtone, a young woman picked up the call immediately.

"Yes. Its Achu", she answered. She was in her early twenties. She had a smart face, with large eyes which she kept attractive with thick kohl applied on their brims. But the kohl was not able to hide the signs of sleep deprivation etched on her face. She wore blue jeans and a loose, plain yellow shirt. She also had a mask covering most of her lower face.

"Yes. I have written the internals today. I knew there was going to be trouble with this pandemic. What? No. I am going by train. Will call you back. Busy." Hell with this pandemic, Achu thought.

*'College was on the verge of examinations and if they were over, in the very least there would have been peace of mind. And Gayathri, I was supposed to propose to her this evening. I should have proposed to her when I had the chance. That chance was gone and now I am going back to my family who thinks that I am not "normal" and a marriage will fix all my problems.'*

"Where to?' A man inside the counter barked.

Alarmed at the bitter tone, she replied "Kaayamkulam."

With a quick motion of professional expertise, the man handed her a ticket. Exchanging her money for the ticket, Achu shook herself out of the queue and embarked on the train.

Ernad Express was speeding up. Even from the distance one could see that the train was crowded. All the people had masks on their faces. Though they tried to maintain distance, it was impossible. There was not even a little breathing room in the crowd. Everyone was disgruntled. Of course, had the train not been crowded, even then everyone would have some problem or the other. That is the general law. Some mouths were murmuring, some eyes were dozing and many ears were listening to music.

"Oh! Can't you keep your bag on the railing above?", a man asked a middle-aged woman beside him in a very irritated voice.

"I will get down two stations from here. Plus, there is not a bit of space on the railing. Where do you want me to keep this bag in this crowd? On your head?", the women replied with visible annoyance at being accused of being a social nuisance. The woman wore a saree. She was fat and had thick hands which she clung around her bag. With thick framed spectacles and shrewd little eyes, she had an air of experience around her.

"He has been complaining ever since he got on this train.", a young boy next to her whispered.

"Then maybe he is riding a crowded train for the first time" she replied.

"Where is your destination?"

"Karunagapally. What about you?"

"Naagarkovil. What is your name?"

"Achu Archana"

"I am Sidharth. Going home?"

"Yes"

"You should have chosen a corner with less complaints Achu *chechi*", he smirked.

She smiled. "I am not new to complaints. I hear them every day. I am a government staff.", she smiled and turned her eyes away from the young man towards the oblivion outside the train windows.

*Though there is a long list of complaining people in this job, I was happy and now I have this unexpected vacation. I am going back to my house where he is keenly waiting. My husband, the sadist, who tortures me for pleasure and my mother-in-law who finds utmost happiness in my pain. Amma please give me the strength to survive for my son.'*

"Achu chechi, its Karunagapally" the young man called out in urgency.

Like a flexible gymnast, she squeezed her way out towards the train door. Many people were getting off on this station and even more people were crowding near the door, ready to attack any time now in a bid to get on the train. Achu had a hard time in the crowd. Her saree was dishevelled. At last, she did the impossible task of getting down on the platform. Fixing her saree, she walked with unsteady steps out of the station.

The night was gorgeous. There was a cool breeze making its way through the land. Leaves murmured and owls hooted. Moon was shining on everything like a supervisor who was in charge of the evening shift in a factory. Moon light made the lane below look beautiful and pale. It was a vast lane spreading its way to a mass of houses grouped together. The lane was not empty. An old woman who had hair as pale as the moon was strode slowly towards the mass of houses. She wore an old and tattered saree with a loose blouse. She had a visibly tired body and a pale face. Both her hands were occupied by bags which carried vegetables, fruits and snacks. The bag was filled to its brim. Two tomatoes were at the very edge and bound to fall on the ground at any second. A few men were there too. They were in groups, some talking rapidly about the pandemic. Others were busy on their phones, shouting orders to kill through their earphones. One of them spotted the old lady and called out.

"Achu maami, where did you go on this night?"

Startled at the sound, the lady turned to its source and passed a smile.

"Oh! It was you. Everyone is coming home *mone*. So I thought I will buy something for the kids"

"That's good news. Do you need help with that luggage, maami?"

"No, it's okay. Thank you". With that, she continued her walk.

*'Ever since Raviyettan died, I have been completely alone. The daily life of loneliness was turning me mad. It was at that point this pandemic surfaced. Now the schools are closed and so my grandchildren will stay with me during the coming days.'*

Happy at her own luck, Achu quickened her pace and entered a large home with blue walls. Becoming a speck, an insignificant mass, an omniscient narrator for a world within a roof. []

**MALAVIKA V R** is a postgraduate Student in MA (English Language and Literature) at Sree Sankaracharya University of Sanskrit. She blogs at myexistence70.wordpress.com

# SHALLOW WATER

## NILES REDDICK

loved the way the water felt on my ankles, the sand beneath the saltwater squishing between my toes, and the occasional minnow that nibbled at the hair on my youthful legs. I'm reminded of this as I soak my feet and have them massaged in the baby blue spa the nursing home put next to my chair to help with neuropathy. The past few months, the stinging pains and cramps at night have diminished.

The head nurse has a great sense of humor. She introduces the Bingo game by singing the rhyme all the patients recall: "There was a farmer who had a dog. And Bingo was his name-o. B…I…NGO, B…I…NGO, B…I…NGO. And Bingo was his name-o." She tells us the staff will be stationed in the halls, and if we get Bingo, yell and one of them will check the card. There're some sugar free snacks as prizes, some picture frames, and some crossword puzzle magazines. I'm hoping for the sugar free snacks.

The media is covering the no visitation rule put in place nationwide because of Corona, and they are making it sound sad that families can't visit usand that patients are lonely and depressed. Such a misrepresentation of the truth. We were depressed before Corona, but not because of the lack of visitors, but because of the end of life.

The nursing home set us up with Skype on our i-pads in case our families wanted to check in virtually, but the fact is that this gives most of our family's justification for not visiting. I don't blame them. I didn't want to visit

103

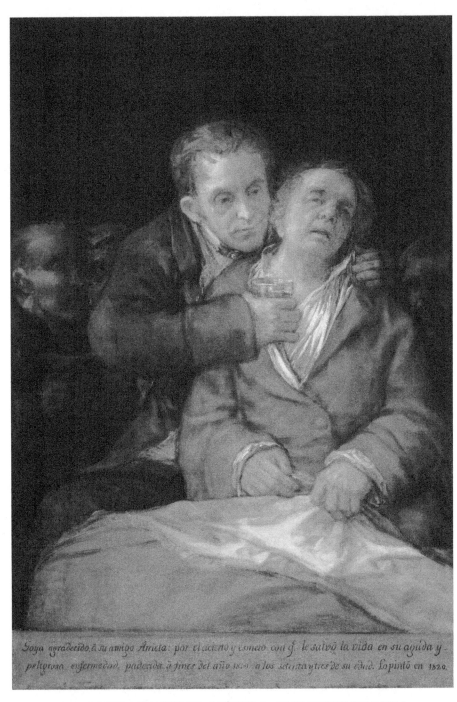

Goya agradecido, á su amigo Arieta: por el acierto y esmero con q.ᵉ le salvó la vida en su aguda y peligrosa enfermedad, padecida á fines del año 1819, á los setenta y tres de su edad. Lo pintó en 1820.

**SELF-PORTRAIT WITH DR ARIETTA** *by* **FRANCISCO DE GOYA**

my parents or grandparents either because it was a stark reminder of the future and here it is smacking me in the face. I'd give anything to have parents and grandparents back to wade beyond the shallows and have some deep, meaningful conversations with them.

When the grandkids come, they are antsy because there's nothing to do. They swing their legs back and forth in the chairs or on the bed, adults shift from one foot to the other, signifying their desire to walk and run out of here. We talk about weather, some headline in the news, or how school or work is going. They don't want to know how non-essential they really are in their own lives, to the companies they've given their own lives to in exchange for some cake and a trinket at retirement. They don't want to hear how quickly life passes.

There's not much to tell them about my life in the home, and they don't want to hear that old Lester coded after a long fight or poor Essie doesn't even know who she is. They want to keep good memories of them in town--Lester the high school football coach who won the state championships more than anyone in the history of the school and Essie who ran the pharmacy and helped more people get medicine, even those who didn't have the money, because she ran tabs when people said stop, get a debit card reader, so she would get paid immediately and not get bad checks.

My son called on the phone last night. "I would have Skyped, but I thought you might be sleeping." I didn't want to tell him, "Well, why the hell did you call me then?" I told him I appreciated it, we made a little small talk, and he said this Corona scare would pass, like everything, and we'd get back to normal. I wanted to tell him this Corona scare might be the best thing yet because it highlighted how abnormal life really was, but I didn't tell him that. I hoped he was right because I would like for them to take me to the beach one more time. I even dream about it, but instead of wading in the shallows, I walk further out until the undertow pulls me into the deep water where I dog paddle until I get cramps and can't. Then, I drift down toward the bottom, holding my last air until I can't, and the last thing I watch is the sun's light grow dimmer until it's fine as a pencil point, and the light goes out.

I heard the nurse call 0-2, and I yelled, "BINGO".

"Congratulations, Mr. Max," the orderly said. "I'll take your card to the nurse and get you a prize."

"I want the sugar free candy," I told him.

"Yes, sir."

When he returned with the bag of sugar free chocolate turtles, I smirked. "They give me diarrhea."

"That's all they got. You want one of the crossword puzzles or one of the picture frames?"

"No, that's alright."

"Go easy on that toilet paper, Mr. Max. We won't be getting any more. Might have to go to wet wash cloths."

"Shit." []

**NILES REDDICK** is author of the novel *Drifting too far from the Shore*, two collections *Reading the Coffee Grounds* and *Road Kill Art and Other Oddities*, and a novella *Lead Me Home*. His work has been featured in thirteen anthologies, twenty-one countries, and in over three hundred publications including *The Saturday Evening Post, PIF, New Reader Magazine, Forth Magazine, Boston Literary Magazine, Flash Fiction Magazine, With Painted Words*, among many others. Visit http://nilesreddick.com/

# REALLY?

## ZÉLIA DE SOUSA

'**H**ow was your weekend?' Asks a key-worker colleague.
'The same as every weekend – Skype city, spring cleaning, DIY, exercise'. Continuing I ask coldly.

'How was yours?'

'Oh, the same'

'Really!'

'Yes?' Answering nervously.

'YOU visit family &friends – have the cheek and audacity to mock those who do the same, and you want THEM to pay the penalty?!… As much as I miss my family & friends, I will NOT break the pandemic rule: *Stay Home – Saves Life's*… So, I ask you again, how was your weekend?'

'How do I know you too are not breaking the rules?' Trying to cover themselves up.

'Once this is all over, I will be going to the police station receiving an affidavit stating: – *I did not break the COVID-19 rule*… Dare to join me?' []

**ZÉLIA DE SOUSA** is a Portuguese/South African now living in the United Kingdom. Brazilian Author Paulo Coelho inspired her to write after reading The Alchemist. She likes to write long/short stories, poetry and scripts. Zélia loves travelling and turning her adventures into stories. Her work has been published in Anthologies, Anti-Heroin Chic Magazine & Another Chicago Magazine. She has contributed to The Loneliness publishing magazine project and is acknowledged in the memoir The True Adventures of Gidon Lev: A Holocaust Survivor.

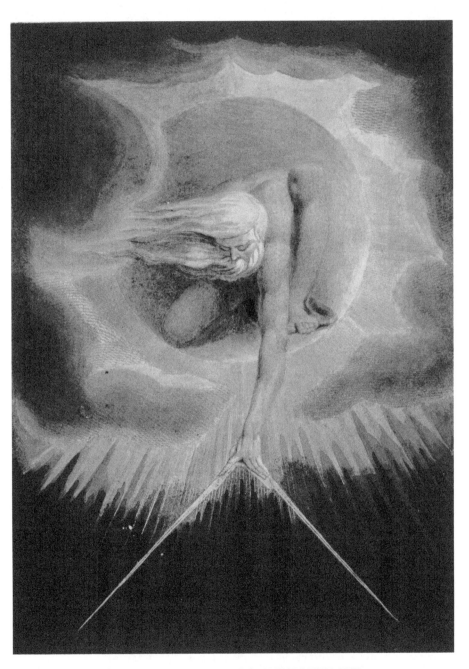

**THE ANCIENT OF DAYS** *by* **WILLIAM BLAKE**

# THE DAY WE LEARNED TO WASH OUR HANDS

## ELIZABETH ROBYN STANTON

The Universal creator took a paint brush and flicked it across the world. It landed where it did. The people didn't see it coming, even though it was quite a bright white, it wasn't until it landed on the skin that it came into awareness. Still many just looked at the afflicted and decided, while it's not me, I will not bother. The word on the street was, it's those people over there, it's how they live, it's what they eat, it's their fault. It's their governments fault, it's their religion, it's not me or mine.

Wash your hands, spray enough bleach to poison, wear gloves, no don't wear gloves, wear a mask, no maybe, okay. Social distance, 6 feet, no ten, no just stand on the marker. Stay home, no don't, help the weak, no sacrifice them. Do as you are told, no protest the guidelines from the advisors.

It's a pandemic some said, we must shut down and protect the citizens. That's unheard of, it's an election year, we can't close down the economy. Our values are livelihood. The harder you work the more you can have, isn't it? Well at least for some and then there is our billion-dollar industries that filter down to the small man, he has to make his nine dollars an hour, or is it six? What about my investments, my retirement? How do I support my several mansions, my jet, and my image? Remember my values, sacrifice the weak, not the privileged.

109

Our hospitals won't cope. They are not prepared for the uninsured masses that will get sick. Leading the world, is our place, this country is great, I am great, but look other countries are suffering. Other countries are closing their borders. Other countries…that's not us. Nothing touches us, not the entitled. We will be okay. Won't we? We are free, it says so in our Constitution.

The Universal Creator heard the arguments from angels he sent to listen. The angels reminded Him, giving the biblical law to humans was a mistake. But The Creator was listening, compassionate, slow to anger, quick to forgive. A creator who knew what was needed. A creator who had sent the cure before the plague. The Universal Creator flicked the brush again and the paint landed on world leaders, movie stars, rich folk were afflicted. It spread through communities at an alarming rate.

People died. Until everyone was touched by the inevitability, of a plague that treated the world and all its inhabitants as equal. Funerals were attended by one or two. People were grieving alone. Every breath taken was conscious as every breath taken was a risk of breathing in this strange plague.

Schools closed, businesses shut their doors, people were commanded to stay in place. But they didn't, because the laws don't apply to entitled people. Never have. Until the sickness whooshed through communities like something was blowing it into the mouths of babes. Young, old, unhealthy, healthy, rich, poor, black, white, or striped, it was out there.

The dying looked into the eyes of the underpaid, hospital staff, said their last good-byes on the telephone and died alone. The hospital staff, undervalued, absorbed this grief but went on tirelessly. Working, at an hourly rate, sometimes, equal to what the victims spent on daily breakfasts, double choc, low fat, decaf Lattes in swish coffee shops. Food was delivered by the low-income earners, risking their safety. But a five-dollar tip was added to the order, giving meaning to danger money.

When the deceased were laid to rest, they all went into the ground. No one cared whether the water filled plastic bags, enhancing boobs or butt went with them. No one cared whether a face full of botox belied their chronological age. They took none of their worldly goods with them. They were not serenaded, no long speeches, no one was there. The body loaned to them in this life had organs that packed it in, in the end. Rich and poor alike.

The entitled didn't reflect, they protested their freedom to move about and return their kids to school and to go back to work. Work to live, not live to work. The great nation, the greatest in the world was coming to a standstill. The culture of entitlement was not working. Other countries controlled the spread. Punishing those who endangered others. But the great leader, of the greatest country on earth, just said, it's an election year, it's not my fault, thank me, let me set the example as he stood next to people, refused to wear a mask and said protest the restrictions.

The casualties grew in number, people were afraid, locked up in their homes in a country known for its freedom, to carry guns, to openly speak what was on one's mind, to earn huge sums of money or tiny sums depending on…well themselves. Anyone can be the President of this fine land. Just work hard. And so, the hospital staff did work hard, and the delivery people, the shelf stackers, the policeman, the fireman all essential services worked double shifts sometimes.

The population were hungry because the culture valued each man to his own means. Universal education was bad enough, government involvement should be minimal. But it was not now. Now the leaders were required to tell the masses what to do. Required to pour money into a flagging economy. Everyone's freedom, everyone's livelihood, everyone's health, was threatened.

Things were not good. Entitlement was being threatened. Empathy was the new value, but it was not a commodity to be traded. It was the cure to the plague. When people half covered in the paint splatter, reflected on their humanity, they saw the other. Individuals perfectly covered in the paint from head to toe, were declared safe. They were safe because now everyone could see their selfishness and would treat them accordingly. Only the Universal Creator could, and would, protect them. []

**ELIZABETH ROBYN STANTON** aka Robyn Singer Rose is a writer and Australian psychologist. She has published short stories internationally and won and placed in competitions. The most notable of her wins is The Hal Porter short story prize where her win and bio were featured in the local newspaper. She has completed a manuscript, a psychological thriller, titled, Salted Pineapple, favourably appraised by Australian novelist, Venero Armano. She lives in Houston, Texas but makes frequent trips back to Australia. Visit http://www.elizabethrobynstanton.com

**SAINT ROSALIE** *by* **ANTHONY VAN DYCK**

# PRAYING FOR RECOVERY

## ANINDITA SARKAR

He saw his mother through the glass window of the intensive care unit. She was lying with calm on her face, wrapped in a light blanket, a mechanical ventilator feeding her lungs ceaselessly. He realized that her pain had subsided and felt a little optimistic He saw men in white hazmat suits cruising in and out of the unit with no scope for a conversation. The sky was darkening ominously, almost like a warning. He needed to depart.

It became a nightly ritual for him to visit his mother, in the hospital. The stench of the antiseptic cleansers no longer bothered him. Suddenly his eyes met his mother's. She had a broad, innocent smile on her face. He stood numb for a while, trying to forge a path of escape. He didn't want to greet her. He hurriedly removed himself from the main corridor. People were scattered in groups in the almost secluded waiting room comforting each other, waiting for a verdict. He swiftly descended the stairs like a river welding through a valley, his head sunk between his shoulders, a deep sigh on his face. The receptionist at the desk was glued to the telephone evidently talking to a friend and not a customer.

As he stepped out, the black sky suddenly illuminated with zig-zag thunders, cars' headlights beamed vividly, the street lamps blazed on the empty asphalt sidewalk. He adjusted his eyes to the blinding bursts of light and walked on towards his destination. A flock of tawny birds was flying back to

113

their abode, fighting against the cold breeze. He watched them till they were gone and only the sound of the flapping of wings and ruffling of feathers lingered. A group of small bats skimmed through the sky, as a part of their nocturnal adventure. He paused briefly in front of the crossing. Feeling lost, he searched for signs of the path towards his destination as the streets ahead seemed confusing.

He passed a café where there were no human diners but mannequins at the tables. Nobody dined out, people had swapped romantic dinners for homemade food. The city had no time for intimacy, the pandemic was to be blamed. It started raining, he spotted one or two people on the road running for shelter. The drizzle obscured their features but the masks on their faces were noticeable. Notwithstanding the rain, he braved the squalls clasping his arms together in his long grey coat, certain that he was on the right track. His hairs were wet, hung damp over his shoulders.

He finally found himself on the edge of a vast expanse, barricaded by a moss-laden black fence. There was no one around. It was a makeshift graveyard strewn with mounds. He took a moment to gaze at the headstones. Almost all of them were strewn with clumps of flowers, except his. He sank onto his knees, filled with despair. "I hope you get well soon mother. I don't want you to be here", he mumbled in a feeble attempt at self-reassurance and slowly melted into the earth. []

**ANINDITA SARKAR** is a Research Scholar pursuing her Mphil from Jadavpur University India. Her works have appeared in The Bombay Review, Litbreak, Pif Magazine, Rigorous, Poetry Potion Review among others.

# LONG PAUSE

## KAMAL ABDUL NASIR

The rain-bearing clouds floated like bales of cotton in the sky… Jane was no cloud-reader but she sensed an imminent apocalypse.

Jane was tall and sinewy with a high cheek bone. She hailed from Goa but she lived in Mumbai. She worked in a local web portal and apart from the hack work of writing 'literature in a hurry', she was an aspiring writer. She had even published some of her stories online.

Jane lived on the 7th floor of Galaxy apartments. Most of the house-maids and servants working in these apartments lived across the street. Jane knew some of these characters because of her maid who was a chatterbox and shared their stories with her. Most of them or their forefathers were actually construction labourers who continued to stay on in the temporary hutments.

Since December 2019, Jane followed the Covid-19 story in Wuhan with a distant interest but as soon as the W.H.O. declared the Novel Corona Virus as a pandemic, she felt she had become a character in a gripping plot.

"All the world is a stage", she mumbled to herself and began to write a news report about Corona Virus:

Right now, we are all in the grips of a worldwide Corona or Covid-19 pandemic as I jot down these words-the plot is still unfolding.

What started as an outbreak in China near the end of 2019 has now become a global pandemic. On March 11, the World Health Organization (WHO) advised that this disease has the characteristics of a pandemic.

**DR BEAKY OF ROME** by **PAUL FÜRST**

From Europe's Black Death during the Middle Ages to the Spanish flu around the time of the First World War, pandemics can change the course of society for many years to come.

The governments everywhere, except Antarctica, have restricted free movement and placed populations under lockdown to limit the spread of the pandemic. The current pandemic, COVID-19, is causing disruption across the entire world.

How could a barely visible, half-dead virus paralyze the whole world? I just wonder. I have started fantasizing about the spiked Corona Virus as a new king of the whole world, wearing a crown as shown in the magnified illustration.

The Virus maybe barely alive but it has the survival skills of any organism on the planet-as the world gears to exterminate the virus, it keeps mutating, like a chameleon, and has mutated over 30 times already!

Can we learn a lesson or two from the deadly virus-how to change, adapt and survive, maybe?

Are we making a mountain of a molehill, or is it going to turn out like the dinosaurs in Jurassic Park?

Being an eternal doubter and a staunch believer in uncertainty, I have started thinking about the various schools of thought on the subject and the conspiracies. How does an individual live with mystery in a mass culture, obsessed with certainty?

What was the world like before the Novel Corona virus took over?

Wars

Jingoism

Broken relationships

Overdependence on technology

Rampant overconsumption

Global warming

But as the pandemic struck and people were forced into lockdown, they have started to speak to each other a lot more, especially loved ones. The planet has started to recuperate as factories and industries paused.

How has a virus brought the whole world together, although affecting each country differently?

The least developed and developing countries are badly affected, resulting in mass exodus from urban areas. Even the highly developed countries have started showing cracks after 3 months. The narrative remained pretty much the same everywhere.

Like all crises, this one has brought out both the worst and the best in human nature. Though many were paralyzed by terror and cowered in their homes, fearful even to shop for groceries, there were health care professionals, police, army and many other citizens who placed themselves in danger in order to help.

Others have made generous donations of money to people they had never met. Many women and even some men volunteered to sew masks, of which there was a shortage, to help those most at risk.

#StayHome #StaySafe.

After filing her story for the day online, she sat in her balcony and looked outside. The curtains on the doors fluttered in the evening breeze from an unusually calm sea.

The rows of street lights stood like obedient soldiers. The roads were deserted. The birds chirped in the twilight. An eerie silence enveloped the dusk.

Some stray dogs moved about, reclaiming the territory, barking at the patrol who shooed them away with the wave of a baton. Once in a while, a Mobile Van sped away into the horizon, piercing the silence with the siren.

She pulled the curtains and switched the lights on, picked up the remote of her android TV and started surfing through the channels.

The news made her sick so she started watching a movie.

Even the movie playing on TV, 'Contagion', was an imitation of real life, more vivid and almost prophetic.

Jane thought of Coleridge who theorized that all art required, "Willing suspension of disbelief". But when life starts imitating art, maybe you don't. She was amused at the idea.

She changed the channel and started watching a TED Talk by Stuart Firstein. Jane was shocked by synchronicity. Firstein was saying, "It's a wonderful idea: thoroughly conscious ignorance". He quoted Karl Poppers:

"All things living are in search of a better world. Men, animals, plants, even unicellular organisms are constantly active."

Suddenly she felt she heard a buzz on her Skype and pressed 'PAUSE' on the remote of her TV and woke up her sleeping laptop.

Sam, Rohit and Nitin were online. She joined the chat on her Zoom app.

She was so relieved to get a reprieve from her cerebral soliloquy and thought of discussing and thinking aloud with her office buddies.

All three lived together and shared the rent of their sea-facing apartment.

She unmuted the screen and waved to all three, moving around in their shorts and Tees.

"How's life?", Sam asked, beaming.

"I am so glad you guys called. I am becoming kinda paranoid".

"Hey Jane, Don't watch too much TV", Nitin advised." I see your TV is on in the background."

"Oh that....I was watching a Ted Talk. Now my TV is on a long pause."

"Your TV is on a pause. Our life is on a pause!" Sam giggled.

"The whole world is on a long pause!" Rohit chuckled.

"It's not funny though", Jane tried to sober things up.

Jane vibed positively with Sam who was also from a literature background and dotted his conversation with poetic concepts. Nitin and Rohit kept the conversation grounded and down-to-earth whenever Jane and Sam became too abstract.

"You know Jane, Sam did a story about the migrants today. Then he sat and cried. A man walked all the way to Bihar, carrying his pregnant wife on a cart, fitted with ball-bearings!"

"I also posted a general feature about Covid-19. I am becoming so obsessed with this. I can't sleep at night. I have also started a short story around some desperate characters during the Lockdown. Do you wanna hear? The name of the story is "Lockdown". O.K.?

"Okey dok. Go on."

Jane started reading:

A group of four men sat huddled, smoking a huqqa (smoking pipe) outside their makeshift hut.

"What should we do? Three months into the Lockdown now...," Anil said, thinking aloud.

"What can we do? Everything is shut down. No daily wages. No work." Sudhir chimed in.

Anil passed the huqqa to Billu.

Billu took a few long and heavy drags and passed to Gautam.

"Let's go and see what we can grab in the dark of night," declared Sudhir, with a glint of hope in his eyes.

"I am a locksmith and know how to open locks. Let's see what destiny has in store for us."

All the four got up at dawn and with covered faces, started walking towards the market. The curfew was enforced from 9 p.m. to 7 a.m., so they had about two hours. Sudhir carried a bunch of keys and Billu carried a crow bar. Anil and Gautam carried two gunny bags for the booty.

After scouting for some time, Anil pointed to a shop with a neon-lit signboard of jewellery. As the three stood together to hide Sudhir, he got busy in trying to unlock the shutter. He tried many keys and then with the help of a key and a wire, he was finally able to work the lock. Sudhir immediately signalled Gautam to pull the shutter up and Anil was told to stay outside and keep an eye on both sides of the road. He noticed a CCTV camera and told Gautam about it. Billu assured everyone not to worry that since their faces were covered.

The shutter was pulled down again after their entry. Sudhir told Anil to sit against the shutter and pretend to sleep. He covered himself with a blanket to hide the open locks. He kept looking around though.

The shop was nearly empty as the owners had probably taken away most of the jewellery to a safer place. A show window displayed some anklets, rings and bangles made of old silver. A few gold rings and loose change and some currency notes were strewn inside a drawer too. Gautam and Billu shoved everything in their gunny bags.

All three stopped in their tracks when they heard Anil knocking on the shutter.

They went close to the shutter and tried to listen. A policeman was trying to wake Anil up who pretended to be fast asleep. After banging the shutter, the cop marched on. All three held their breath and heard the sound of heavy boots fading away.

After what seemed like an eternity, Anil knocked on the shutter and told them to come out. They pulled the shutter up and came out and put the locks back on the shutter. They started walking back with the booty hidden in a blanket. A vegetable vendor was getting ready to start his day. All of them bought some turnip, potatoes and onion. A policeman came and asked the vendor why he had opened the shop so early when the curfew time is up to 7 a.m. Anil started bargaining for the veggies to convey a sense of normalcy. The policeman asked Gautam to cover his face and always wear a mask when he was out. Billu coughed and sneezed. The policeman got visibly horrified and walked away.

The next day, all four of them got up late and saw the news of a robbery on TV.

The shopkeeper exaggerated the amount of stolen goods as the camera showed a nearly empty shop. For one week, none of them ventured out.

After a week or so, Billu went out to buy some essential items, after 4 p.m.

He was stopped near the roundabout by a policeman who told him to get himself tested. Billu felt relieved because he was thinking of a worse scenario.

A health worker pointed a digital thermometer to his forehead. Two hands from inside the van took a swab of his nose and throat. Billu sneezed when tickled by the swab. One health worker immediately told him to sit in the van. Billu's phone was taken away for contact tracing.

Anil, Sudhir and Gautam's numbers popped up and they were immediately called. The voice on the other side informed them that Billu was in their custody and asked for their whereabouts.

All three were petrified. Sudhir immediately hid the booty under a cot. When Gautam asked where they had to go, he was given the name of the hospital. All three heaved a sigh of relief. They were told that Billu was being taken to the hospital as he seemed to be Corona positive. All his contacts must be tested too.

After tests, all the three were advised to quarantine themselves for 2 weeks as there were no beds in the hospital. Billu was let off too.

"Wow….Jane!", all three exclaimed. Is that all?"

"Well, I am kinda stuck here. Writer's Block". Maybe they will go and have some fun on Falkland Road or maybe buy some essential supplies. I dunno. Maybe they will be caught somehow. LOL."

"Where did you find these characters?" Sam asked.

"Well, the characters are modelled on these construction labourers who live across the street. Most of them have gone back home."

Jane had an irresistible urge to sneeze. She couldn't control and sneezed.

"What a loud sneeze, Jane. Wow. Do you know what a big sneeze like that means?"

"Well, I know this is one of the symptoms of Covid-19".

"You may be asymptomatic and still be positive", Rohit offered his expert opinion.

Sam looked worried and told Jane, "I am worried about you, my dear. Should I call an ambulance?"

"Nah….I don't think a simple sneeze is anything to worry about. A very high fever is a sure sign, though".

Within minutes, Jane heard a knock on the door. She told her friends, "Excuse me. I have to get the door".

Three health professionals in PPE Kits pointed a digital thermometer at her forehead and as the light turned RED, the two accompanying nurses asked Jane to get ready to move to the nearby hospital.

"Hospital! Why do I have to come to the hospital?"

"You shall be tested for Covid-19. Please don't panic. You may be quarantined and treated in the hospital," one of the nurses explained.

"Who informed you about me, may I know?"

"Maybe your neighbour. Your friend, maybe… we don't know".

Jane told her friends on video chat the consequence of a loud sneeze. Sam told her not to worry as all three were on the way too. Rohit told her to take a couple of change of clothes, her mobile and a bottle of water.

Jane tried to convince and persuade the nurses that sneezing can be fixed by a simple home cure like smelling mint and steam. The nurse showed her hands, implying, "Talk to my hands". Before being taken away, Jane asked the nurses if she could be granted 5 minutes to feed the stray dogs. She rushed in and gathered together bread, milk and some rice and put everything in a big plate outside the door. The stray dogs acknowledged her gesture by wagging their tails, barked and ran after her van.

As she lay stretched out in the back of the Mobile Van, one of the nurses took her phone for contact tracing and sent the information to the concerned official department. Jane could see from her stretcher the pinnacle of trees swishing by in the glass window and she could hear the siren blaring through the streets.

The Van screeched to a halt and as she was wheeled out on the stretcher, she was pleasantly surprised to see Sam. Jane told him to inform her family and asked about Nitin and Rohit. Sam told her that both of them were there already and talking to the administrative staff who seemed to have informed them that there were no beds available.

"Now what?" Jane asked.

"Don't worry. You may be taken to some other hospital," Sam tried to calm her down.

A nurse came and told Sam to keep a distance.

A policeman who was patrolling the area fined Sam for not wearing a mask. Sam tried to explain that he was, in fact, carrying a mask that he was about to wear and even showed it to him.

The policeman asked him for an ID and when Sam showed him his Press card, the cop relented and instructed him to keep wearing a mask.

A nurse overheard the conversation and told the staff. Suddenly the scenario changed. The hospital staff did not want a sting op by the media. The matter was discussed with senior doctors and administration.

Jane was getting restless and paranoid. Rohit and Nitin came and informed her that the hospital did not have a bed. She may be taken to a different hospital. Jane thanked both of them.

As all the four waited outside, a doctor wearing a PPE Kit came and told Jane to self-isolate in her own home for two weeks and wrote a prescription.

Everyone felt relieved. Sam brought his car and all four went back to Jane's apartment and dropped her.

Jane received a call from her mother who informed her that since no trains or flights were available, no one would be able come over in order to take care of her.

Jane informed her that there was no need as she was back home and had been advised self-isolation for two weeks.

Two weeks. How time expands sometimes.

Jane received a call from her office to take care of herself and take it easy for two weeks. She sat outside on her balcony after taking her medicines. Her mild flu was fully cured after she started smelling mint, popping a lot of vitamin C and drinking lukewarm water as advised by her mother.

Jane looked outside and saw four friends sitting outside their hut and enjoying huqqa (smoking pipe) and probably drinks too. They seemed to have misheard the advice of using alcohol.

She felt drowsy and lay down on her bed.

In the twilight of dream and wakefulness, Jane heard a bodiless voice.

"Do you like my story?"

"What story?"

"Don't you think you are now part of a gripping plot? The whole world is a stage and you are one of the characters."

"You are misquoting Shakespeare. Do you mean you are the bacteria or virus or whatever? Are you nearby? Why are you talking to me?"

"Well, you human species may call me by whatever name. Magnify me a hundred thousand times. Do you see me now? Barely alive, half-dead. But just to give you a hint, do you see my spikes? Do you see my crown? I am a king.

A miniaturized version, more powerful than your kings and more deadly than your weapons of mass destruction, lethal enough to decimate human species."

"Can I call the media? They would love to grill you."

"Don't bother. I hate paparazzi. I like to live below the radar."

"But why are you on the killing spree?"

"I am your nemesis."

"Are you Voldemort? Oh! Are you the Nemesis Virus from Resident Evil 3?"

"No. I am Nemesis, the daughter of Night. I personify conscience, moral reverence for law, the natural fear of committing a culpable action, always mentioned with Aidôs which you know as Shame."

"Oh Nemesis, I know you, you are a kind of fatal divinity! O Cygnus in the constellation, O beautiful Swan. You were seduced by Zeus and then flew away. Because he was seen by men flying high in the sky, they said he was put in the stars. You bore an egg which was thrown in Leda's lap. From it sprang Helen, who excelled all other girls in beauty. Oh Nemesis! I am so glad I met you."

"Yes, how do you know my story in such great detail?"

"Well, I did my Master's in English Literature and I read the poem by W.B. Yeats, 'Leda and the Swan,'" Jane said modestly.

"Yes, I direct human affairs in such a manner as to restore the right equilibrium wherever it has been disturbed."

"But why are you hell-bent on decimating humanity?"

"Do I have to enumerate? What has your species been up to? You have been killing each other in endless wars. You have no sense of reverence for nature. While other species are happy just continuing the species, you have this passion, this obsession to continue your name by hook or by crook. Some of you do this by good deeds but some go to extreme lengths.

You are totally bereft of kindness. You are so power hungry. You fight in the name of religion. You glorify violence. You are so jingoistic. You hoard the riches as the rest of humanity starves... Oh well, my job is not to justify what I do. When I am called upon to action, things have already gone beyond the warning stage."

"Are you an ally of the dragon? Are you a punishment from God?"

"No. I am your own creation, man-made. A designer cocktail of many strains. God has no role to play in this. You are being punished for your own actions. Do you like my story?"

"The plot is still unfolding", she replied, drank some water and went back to sleep.

The voice seemed to fade away. []

Based in Delhi, **KAMAL ABDUL NASIR** is an MA in English Literature from Delhi University and has studied Mass Communication from Jamia Millia Islamia. A poet, filmmaker and storyteller, he is also a cultural and eco-activist. He has been teaching media in various universities for last 10 years.

# POETRY

# ALAN PERRY

## COVID Wing - Day 97

Lines on her face
trace the straps she curls
over her ears, tightening
the medicinal-smelling mask
around her nose, across her cheeks
under her chin. A face shield
tightly banded on her forehead
reflects what lies in front of her.
Hard to breathe, harder still
for her patients, their lines
in the hall grow longer each day.
More tubing to connect, intubations
to perform, rotation of the dead
with the near-dying--hallway
to room to hallway, and again.
Her voice is muffled as she holds
an iPad in front of the patient
encouraging his relatives to say
words she's heard before.
No one can read her face
under the mask, the turning corners
of her mouth as breath fades
biting her lip when the patient
no longer inhales.
Droplets run past her nose
into the absorbent mask.
Her goggles fog up
from the heat, the heaviness
of what she must wear. []

First published in *Global Poemic*, 2020

# ANN PRIVATEER

## I'll Show Them

The planet's on fire
They need a lesson before dying
Untethered souls as they might be

Where is the permanence we were
born into? Those of us who refused to
"step on a crack, you'll break your mother's
back"? But we grew up with plastic everything,
                              radical getting and speeding.
How many cars does one person need?

We feared 2000 might mean the end
But life went on and so did we, unhinged
Unheading that we, the planet, was walking off a cliff!
                              Even Greta the young
Girl who made sense but...change, what
me? I'll never change my ways, the planet
will be yours, young folks, you do it. []

# BAISALI CHATTERJEE DUTT

## Carpe Annum

It was the year when touch could kill.
Hugs had been registered
as biological weapons of warfare.
As touch faded,          so did eye-contact
for smiles had been frozen          into cement walls.

It was the year of mass pain
and global confusion.
Sex was sanitised,
pleasure, euthanized,
pain, wholesale
kisses from your grandmother, poison
and sighs
were the last breaths          of those who died          without saying
                                                                                                goodbye.

Our children learnt to see and write          in pixels,
speaking          in          hashtags          and          emojis,
speech evaporating
like Arctic ice.

Movies bloomed, that year,
in abundance,
clothes lost their vanity,
shrinking in the closets,
and men learnt to cook,          clean          and          wipe baby bottoms.
Not all men          though.
Some continued to chew rusted nails
and speak through leather,
their hands, twin deliverers
of goosebumps          and the chokehold.

The women
continued picking up fragments,
sewing together peaceable moments
in their families' fractured lives,
through music            and a hearty minestrone,
using the leftover threads
to stitch the frayed pieces of their sanity
onto their patchwork, mismatched doormats.

It was a year like all others,
when women could not quit
because the unicorns never came. []

## Magic Carpet Ride

How about a cab ride
backwards,
to the time
and place
before all this?
When fights were all about
money,
making up was about
sex
and love
was a movie and ice-cream?

A yellow cab ride,
to a time
and place
where staring out it's window
and looking at the rain
meant wet shoes
and hot soup.

A magic cab ride,
to a time
and place
where breath
wasn't poison
and hugs weren't weapons.

Call me a cab, lover,
and let's just grab a ride
to the fringes
of another time,
another place. []

# BHISMA UPRETI

## Pandemic and Love

Pulling us together
the hunger of creativity
had almost brought us closer.
Because of love
our trembled hot lips were seemingly
connecting each other.
Both hearts had seemed to be singing one song.

The air of pandemic came as a storm
which swept many things
and tore many lives and dreams.

Like flying feather by storm
we reached far and different islands.
Today, the house built by utmost will
has become a prison.
Doubts and terror as gate keepers
are standing outside the home
The darkness of uncertainty is blanketing us.
But, fighting against this dark, the lamp of faith is still
alive dimly.

In this time,
the invisible seed of pandemic
is becoming more powerful than humans.
If we could save our faith
surely one day our wills will again become *Ardhanarisvara*
and the love will be sparked by its light.
The door of creation will be opened again.

*Ardhanarisvara* : Lord Shiva with Half male (god) and half female
(goddess) form. It is said to be a complete form of God.

Translated by RUPSINGH BHANDARI

# DR. BRAJESH KUMAR GUPTA "MEWADEV"

## I Feel You Come Back Again

The transition through this difficult time
The ones our lives revolve around
These life beliefs must be mourned separately
But that is nothing new
Know that the strain, the pain, will eventually ease
I have hope in death of our love
It is sweet to know that stocks will stand
I am the gentle autumn rain
If there's something I can do,
Real, deep love is, as you know, very unobtrusive,
But our hearts remain the same
I've spent every glorious moment
Remember the love that we once shared,
From the depths of my heart, come the words of a lover,
I hope, from my heart, that your pain will decrease,
Let's draw together to recuperate,
We can make our lives sublime,
We'd have countless things to say
At the end of each life's road;
The only memories that really matter
We all are meant to learn some things,
We turn away, afraid that it might happen to us
I find that peace at the close of day. []

# CHRISTIAN GARDUNO

## One + One = Eleven

When this quarantine is over it's probably better to say CV19 never happened, right? Like, let's just say it was a big flu- we don't need words like "pandemic"- what is a pandemic, anyway? I don't like little doctors in their uppity lab coats running around calling every little thing a PANDEMIC. It was the flu, OK, the flu. And some people used a very limited number of sick days and then it went away. I remember it vividly, the phone call was perfect.

What happened was, and a lot of people don't know this because I'm really not allowed to be talking about this but, you know, when you are President, they only want you talking about certain things, we have big meetings about it all the time- huge meetings- but what happened was- someone got down with an orangutan and it gave him CV19- and by that, I mean, the orangutan gave basically leftover SARS, from Obama's Administration, to the human. It's actually not all that uncommon on the other continents. It's because they play so many violent video games, a lot of people don't know that. You know that before my Presidency, video games had no rating system whatsoever? It was like, insane! We got that cleared up on Day One. Day One. That was the day we locked her up. Beautiful day, there's never been a day like that.

It's the testing, that's what it is. Nobody wants to pay for it. Why should The Feds pay for it? Makes no sense. It's a states issue. Test your people, get them off Communism, and back to their jobs fluffing the economy. I've been seeing A LOT of new welfare Cadillacs lately, you can't fool me. It's the Deep State that doesn't allow for testing, don't blame me. If it wasn't for me, Hillary Rodham Clinton would still be a free citizen. Day One. I'll tell you what- we'll pay to test Florida, only Florida!! That will piss off Leftie Maoist "Governor" Newsom!!! People have been telling me that this so-called "elected official" (Highest-rated state of illegals "voting" multiple times) actually passed legislation making it mandatory to defecate in the street in California. No lie, I've been hearing this from people all over the country every day, they say, "Sire, we want our personal bathrooms back, the streets are all yucky with caca, please, Boss, do something to help us. There's no pooping privacy in California anymore, you were right the whole time, you told us long ago that China was going to own us, you warned us and we didn't listen. We could have avoided this malignant fate by Making America Great Again and buying authorized merchandise, but we went the other way, we wanted our Kenyan King." People tell me that all the time and now you want Daddy to take your temperature? Ain't happening, toots, put down your Karl Marx textbooks and open up those coal factories!! []

# COLLEEN MOYNE

## Still the River Flows

The world is in turmoil.
We shake our heads in disbelief.
This is not the year we chose
but through the chaos, nature flourishes
and the river flows

Fear spreads as quickly
as the threat, keeping us guessing
when it will end. No-one knows,
and yet, like a reassuring friend
the river flows

I seek the solace of its gentleness
at a secret place where no-one else goes
It tells me to breathe, trust.
The world still turns
and the river still flows

The sun still shines
the breeze still blows
communities bond, solidarity shows…
and every day faithfully, tirelessly
the river flows []

# A New Appreciation

I never knew how much I would miss
the smell, the feel
of my favourite book shop
or the familiar face
of the barista at my local café
smiling over steaming coffee


Today, at my local supermarket
I saw plexi-glass screens
between the staff and me
and for the first time, felt the impact
of social distancing
from their perspective


I've never been one
for small talk on the sidewalk
about the weather
or for starting a conversation
just to fill the silence
in the waiting room or queue


Yet, these small things -
so much a part of each day,
when taken away,
become so much more
and we find ourselves counting the days
until that smell, that feel, that small talk returns. []

# DIMPLE D. MAPARI

# A Breaking Break

World badly needed a break
But not at the cost of lives already lost and
And having at stake many others,
World badly needed a break
But not like this...
We needed-
Changed routine but with rest,
not with stress.
Peace of mind and not isolation of this kind,
Humanity and not hunger,
Empathy, Kindness but not enveloped in fear
Gentleness but not guilt,
Silence that is not filled with sadness for the departed
Quietness, but not quarantine
Yesterday we were all close but each individual was an island,
difficult to reach,
Now we are far away from each other but bonded with a strong
bond of care...
To make us understand their worth, Life and Nature have joined
hands in conspiracy...
And returned us forced solidarity, and tranquility....
It is forced hence not fruitful...
I am asked to meditate - that does not help
To concentrate...
The entire world had become a no honking area...
No horns, no hawkers, no whirring wheels...
No school going kids....
No cranky toddlers...
only silence outside and loud noise within,
Why we humans are complicating our already complex lives?
I propose Poetry, patience and a bit of philosophy in these
pandemic times. []

# DONNA NEMMERS

## Dying Alone

Hold your hand up, mid-air, against the pane
and I will do the same
feel only cold glass, warm hands fogging, millimeters separating
ponder eyes reaching, locking, studying, longing
feel your heart rising, throat filling
eyes welling, words leaving

I have only your absence, sorrow hoarded in time
your irrevocable goodbye cast in bronze
my tomorrows released from your hands, your eyes
no longer a window, but a mirror
eternally reflecting back
on all that was loved, and gone away []

## Pestilence

Counting untainted breaths
    against swirling viral forces
whipping winds and rain
    rinse blighted air
streets of isolation pods
    beehive in private
as earth quietly resuscitates
    beneath vacant cities
unarmed doctors wield blind hope
    against pandemonium
white sheets dress angels
    who've traded lungs for wings []

# Vent Death

*Fuck you, Grim-*
ravaging lungs
trading air for phlegm
coercing teetering hearts
into final ticks
metamorphosing
slowly upward,
strangling flesh
and drowning us
in our own congealed juices
as you gloat
in the purging
of plasma and breath.
But oh!
The soul escapes
Unscathed []

# DONNY WINTER

## Carbon Footprint

The sun seems angry this summer
as each day measures in asphalt cracks.
The remaining grass patches
beneath the backyard maples have gone arid
and their crisps are muffled under each footfall
like the pops of bacon in a pan—
        while the Pride flag – bleached
        and frayed, whispers as it waves
        July goodbye on a humid wind.
As I shift with shortening
shadows, I pray with roadside chicory for respite
and sing for rain with a passing oriole whose beak
has grown leaden in this drought—
even the stationary tractor in the field creaks and
hides behind heat ripples like a man-made mirage.
        Dear Planet: let this summer
        pass; let this industrial standstill
        re-invigorate your hope in us—
permit those storm heads to peek above the west
long enough to swallow the sun,
retract these swords of grass to their sheaths,
and give us the baptismal downpour necessary
to soak the brine from our veins, to erode
the walls we build to keep you contained. []

# The Pandemic Academic

The drawn office curtains signal
the show is over, for now,
as the once busy street outside
has become slow, like a creek
silenced by shallowness.

As two laptops cast industrial
light through the office, a forest
of cables drapes across the desk and
strangles the half-drunk coffee mug
like untamed kudzu on a forest floor.

Bird song has finally faded behind
the chime of incoming e-mails,
as each hushed S.O.S. speaks
behind these window screens as
subtle pleads to know when this'll end.

Now, the days are measured digitally
and unmade beds sculpt each circadian
sacrifice – my hands have grown elastic
in their attachment to these keys, as each
anxious response is crafted, yet drastic. []

# DREW PISARRA

## Are You There God?
## It's Me, Everyone

I pray for the people who scar the earth
as I pray for Earth to heal her scars.
I pray for the sick who lash out in hurt
and by sick I mean those who go too far
with greed, and overall lower the bar
because they're what… too scared, too cynical,
I almost typed too mean. Too critical?
Why do we recoil from assigning blame?
More fear? Guess I'll pray again, a radical
prayer for less endemic causes of shame. []

## A Poem of Patience

So they're opening up the Jersey Shore,
and some hair salons near the Finger Lakes
yet who wants to pop in a shop or store,
or drop by at the beach for goodness sake?
Is the quest for a bad haircut so great
that we'd plow ahead to a second wave
and then stand suntanned near an open grave
when simple patience would've done the trick
to deflate that killer curve and to stave
off contagion? Or are we all that sick? []

**TWO POEMS**

# ED O'CASEY

## Reading these obitchiaries
## cuz I got no more novels

What the casket calls death I call anthology -
      Times Herald Post
      Record of Personal
      Micro-Histories,

fifteen minutes on the page a mob scale assault:
I need to check the hand sanitizer aisle
      again. the streets this Wednesday

morning are as dead as the readership of this
      Newspaper - with all those people dying in alphabetical order,
      this story's sure to go viral. I'm trying to write something
      more than a series   of one-liners, but my sense

of self-preservation can't linger long enough on the columns
of names and faces and
      preceded-in-death-by's and
      survived-by's and loving
      father/uncle/husband/daughters.

this could be
      a roster of residents at the assisted living center
or a
      catalog of the phonebook generations.

      I think of my own parents creeping
      toward their 80's, dad's artificial heart
      valve pumping maybe more than blood
      while he tends to his double risk-group
      wife, mom at this moment Zoom-playing
      with her granddaughter in this era crowned
      by
social distance.

surrounded by vectors I shake the newspaper to redefine the creases
   and loosen or remove any little beasties
   that might be hanging on for the ride home. []


# Love in the Crown Age

all these shapely ladies under
their masks at the club tonight
like a Saudi hijab-fest in here.

our mistranslation: the face covering
an emblem of oppression - thousands

line up to die for your right to whine
about how unfair your life seems - to prevent

unnatural desire, the sinful union of unwed
particles, beauty in the eyes of your smile.

my upstairs neighbor races
across the dawnlit parking
lot to return shoes to his booty
call, this morning after partial
reopening in the face of pandemic

gonna lift my mask off my freedom
and exercise my God-given rights!

you sound like you're talking through
socks, but I don't wanna talk no-how.

now all of us strolling along with nonchalant
head nods and the face obscured.

it's a weakness for the unwed to
couple, and I ain't going to die of
this crown crap—I'm too young or
blessed by God. so drop that beat!

        walking to her car
        in the parking lot
        the new girl avoids
        eye contact to join
        church nontraffic
        in her seethrough
        top and Daisy Dukes []

# EDILSON AFONSO FERREIRA

## Rediscovered Paradise

We found ourselves in the deserted streets,
and twinned in the challenge and fearlessness
to the enacted isolation.
Compelled by the oddity of the moment,
we delighted in such a privacy,
fruit and reward for our boldness.
Our love blossomed, suddenly and calmly,
honest, pure and original,
- secluded inhabitants, entrusted by destiny -
to start a new world.
Let time stop, give this dream a lot of rope,
like the new toy we get for Christmas.
Don't be lost the magic, take root in the ground,
bathe in the water that blesses, baptizes and revives.
Let it be heir to the best of our stories,
the best of our hopes. []

# EMILIAN LUNGU

## cyber stockholm syndrome (2)

the only memory i have of you
is the carbon print i create after i print a 3D doppelgänger
of yourself
which by the end of the day gets its polymers severed into
pixels,
fading into photons

the only memory we have of each other
is your finger print on my film camera
i exist only as a ghost caught on film
shot in the intersection of distinct frames
such will not risk overlapping

the only memory you have of me
is the trace of my astral projection in the space you inhabit
this is the only way the body can communicate

i come everyday
mirroring trails

i caress every single object
contaminate them with my presence
of lockdown aficionado []

# GEORGE R. ROSS / VICTORIA CRAWFORD

## Rapunzel

Pen
page
again
in old age,
at hand writing when
home alone, poem alone, engage

clock
hours
tick tock
write flowers
of hope, behind lock—
Rapunzel in Covid Towers []


## Rosemary Isolation

New rosemary planted
in my desert garden
withers despite weeks of care

Son Mark leaves supplies at the gate
we wave and call out
I'm glad he can't see my eyes []

# H.L. DOWLESS

## An Evil Mist Is Moving

The poisonous mist hangs in the air,
the talk around is all lies,
the people may walk outside if they dare,
yet multitudes cough up their lungs and die.

A bleak fog moves o'er our cherished landscape,
this tainted cloud swirls
until it settles into the Grim Reaper's shape;
the confused masses scramble, stumbling across many hurdles
as the diseased lie scattered round in degenerate waste.

The spirit of Satan moves throughout every nation,
a gargantuan wickedness I do declare,
compelling the earth's citizens to remain in their stations,
lest they are condemned into the dungeon, I swear.

The western economy has been crashing since way back in 1983,
when they removed all checks' balances giving the Fascist nations
                                             so much liberty;
yet their leaders claimed the vast unemployment was caused by
                                      a lack of education,
as they turn the individual back around without hesitation.

They command us not to speak to one another,
keeping two yards away or more,
yet I walk into the local market with a cold shudder,
never knowing what the future holds in store.

The real economy faded away in years thirty and five,
massive loans have been all sustaining us,
with no person ever asking why;
by some magic the chronic situation shall improve I trust,
specifically how our leaders only surmise.

Like the need for university this virus creates a handy excuse,
providing cover for an economic system that never improves;
while allowing the same villains to continue their abuse,
since only the rank and file ever lose.

This tainted marriage with its Fascist government,
shall soon be organized by a tyrannical Fabian master.
Unto where shall individual liberty soon be sent?
I anticipate our looming bloody disaster.

I stand before the sacred cross on a mountain top so high,
overlooking the valley of death so far below,
chanting the patriots ancient battle cry
toward that dreary scene,
such a precious vow every freeborn citizen should know;
Live free or die,
forever free! []

# HILARY KING

# The World at Golden Way
### *Our House in Quarantine*

## Kitchen

One morning I wake up and the kitchen is empty. The cabinets beneath the stove, empty. The shelves above the counter, empty. Even the dishrack, these days a dump truck of pots, pans, bowls, spatulas, cake tins, beaters, ramekins, pasta maker and whatever else we used the night before, completely and utterly empty. Only the coffee pot remains, and it's full, the little red light beaming at me, which is weird because I didn't prep the coffee last night. I was too tired. I start to reach for the pot when I hear a clatter. I race to the front door and fling it open just in time to see my favorite wooden spoon and my favorite cookie sheet, scorched and bent, hobbling down the street. Stop, I shout. Come back! I yell. They keep going.

## Square Footage

Glasses accumulate around the house like fingerprints. On the coffee table. On my desk. On my husband's desk. On the washing machine. On the bench by the door. On the bookshelf. On every other surface in the kitchen. Large glasses, small glasses, coffee mugs, tea cups, yellow plastic cups from a barbecue restaurant, a tall glass swirling with the remnants of milky iced coffee, a lowball sticky with scotch, a stemless wine glass, its lip permanently stained red.

## My Closet

Like a dingy disco in some lesser Eastern Bloc country. So many stripes. So many wide-legged pants. The sparkling dreams of a trapped people. Each set of cheap heels seems to have one shoe with a broken strap. Why? What happened? A hook holds a cluster of tiny sequined purses with straps long as reins, the inside of the purses littered with ancient cigarettes and orangey lipsticks. The door here doesn't close all the way.

## Living Room

We leave our shoes outside so that we can keep clean the high-pile of privilege we walk on.

## Garage

My husband counts his worries, finds he doesn't have enough, orders more. The garage fills. Among this miniature mountain range of boxes, he places a yoga mat. Here he meditates. Closes his eyes, lotuses his legs, holds in one palm his instinct and in the other, the Internet. When he opens his eyes, he knows what he needs to order next.

## Housekeeping

Weekends I don't read the news. I clean, scrubbing the bathrooms, the baseboards, the floors.. Facts lurk under the bed. I push them further into the dark, but not too far. Later, I'll want to take them out to the patio, have a drink, and look at them, really look at them. But not yet. Now, Saturday morning, I'm cleaning. I'm moving and removing. At the stove I lift off the heavy grates surrounding the gas rings. With a clean cloth, I wipe from our surfaces all the spills and stains.

## Perhaps the Bathroom

Late in the pandemic, my husband begins talking to himself in the bathroom. Quietly, but forcefully and regularly. He did not do this previously or I was not always nearby previously to hear it. Now his desk is mere feet from the toilet's bowl. Perhaps he carries from the constant stream of meetings a river stone of idea or thought. Perhaps they carry him. Perhaps he goes there to wash away the stink of business. He hates his job, so lacking in art and history and feeling. It's a cloud, this hate, a saturation of emotion in his atmosphere. Perhaps the small room is a rain chamber where the cloud bursts and drains. Perhaps. I don't know what he says. Not listening is how we protect ourselves and others.

## Bed Is a Room

Afternoons, I build a cabin out of my fatigue and lock myself in. Wake me there and I answer in riddles, a sleepwitch. Sometimes I go to my daughter's bed, hot and crowded with her girlhood. I curl my arms around the soft stuffed creatures that live there and let them seep into my dreams. Night brings relief. The house swells and there is room for all of our darkness. I drag my insomnia from room to room, the animals we have tamed following me.

## Walls and Other Things
## That Are Supposed to Remain Upright

My husband's the strongest. Never wavers, always upright in what we must do. My son is also solid. He's fifteen and hates people. He'll always be a door and never a window. My daughter's a mirror, hears too much when sandwiched between her parents in front of the tv every night. Fine, she says. I'm fine, it's fine. She wears her mask to bed at night and dreams of cats washing her hands. I'm the weak spot, parts of me already crumbing, giving way when the wind blows. I'm going out, I tell my husband. This will be how the house falls down.

## Future Museum

Masks of course. The first set, a scramble to get. Simple in cotton, made by hand by a co-worker's wife. Sterilized and left outside before being worn. The next, the rest, branded, logoed, high-fashioned, high tech, low with stink. We hang them from the mantle, upside down holiday.

Two missing puzzle pieces. This is not a metaphor.

Sourdough starter, bought online, named Jane, still hungry, still bubbling, still making the best damn waffles.

Tap dancing, Italian, singing, piano, guitar, math, yoga and everything else we meant to learn.

Toilet paper, paper towels, sanitizer, each still wet tears.

A floor covered in hair. Dog hair, husband hair, son hair, daughter hair, my hair in all its colors.

The dog, dead from walking. []

# HOWIE GOOD

## Reason to Believe

**1**

By late March, tens of thousands
were about to die from the virus.
I was sad, so sad. Then the sun
would come up and the buds open
a little more each day. You could hear
the music – the Mister Softee truck
was out. You just had to watch for it.

**2**

As I go around town,
I see people wearing
face masks all wrong,
under their noses
or even their chins.
I don't want to get
into it with them.
I just want to get away.
Given a choice,
I'd live somewhere
civilized and safe,
somewhere like Switzerland,
but without all the cows
and glaciers.

**3**

It's important to pay attention to possible omens.
Like the tall weed growing across the street,
whose milky white sap is said to relieve pain.
Do you have 30 seconds? I swear sometimes it glows. []

# JANE CARTER

## The bell tolls

We stand apart on pavements, heads bowed as you pass by,
towards the dappled graveyard where with God, in peace you'll lie.

Before you were a stranger, but in death you're so much more,
a fallen comrade who fought our mortal enemy in a terrifying war.

We come together, a kingdom united in battle against
                                        a common foe.
and mourn with all who loved you, a national family joined in woe.

A warrior true, we won't allow the life you gave in conflict
                                        to be discounted.
You're one of us, a person to be remembered, not a number
                                        to be counted.

As brothers we'll fight until the virus is defeated, you'll not have
                                        died in vain.
In victory we'll celebrate the lives of all the fallen, bring comfort
                                        to those in pain.

And as we watch your lonely, final progress we hear
                                        the church bells peel.
We ask for whom the bell tolls. It rings for us, it marks
                                        our shared ordeal. []

# JARED MORNINGSTAR

## Dead End

You used to love driving at night,
to escape ghosts and mundane realities.
The road meant happiness
in the form of exit ramps
and taillights of fellow midnight Kerouacs
in the distance ahead.
Like you, they knew
the world's greatest love song
was the hum of the engine
and the percussion of tires on pavement
with some Willie Nelson playing on the radio;
the welcoming thought that
a goodnight's sleep could be found
at a mom-and-pop motel,
and that a cup of coffee,
a club sandwich,
or both could be served
by a smiling waitress at any hour
where streetlights,
that gorgeous neon,
appeared on the horizon.
Even the smell of gasoline
during an early AM fill-up
would make your heart beat faster,
for as long as that motor was running,
you felt alive.

But the highway is dead now.
Those city lights don't shine anymore;
the 24-Hour Diners are closed,
the jukeboxes no longer play.
You're lucky if you can find

an open McDonald's drive-thru,
where a masked worker
nervously accepts your card
and gives you a greasy burger and fries
that you now wonder if you should even eat.
And there's no room at the motor inn;
it's closed, perhaps permanently,
you can't tell,
but you sure know the road
no longer feels like home:
home is where you're stuck,
in late night silence.
You no longer have the miles ahead
to look forward to when the sun rises;
instead, when your weary head hits the pillow,
all you can do is pray in loneliness
that life will return one day to the interstates,
that this dead end isn't forever,
and that when you wake up,
you'll still be able to breathe. []

# JAY GANDHI

## The Cage

The parrot starts to sing *Paani Da*
as I play the E minor Chord.
He tries to be in tune but the heat
is getting to him. A.C. is not working,
roof is leaking, maid has not turned up,
Zomato guys are taking ages to deliver
a Cheese Frankie. Nick is still in coma.
I shift the chord to D. Though ungainly,
the parrot does finish his song. []

## No Friend in the city

I play squash in my room
with a plastic ball
and table tennis racket.

I self-counsel, pat on my back
and cook *khichdi*
every evening.

Sundays
I read my 10-year-old emails—
Sent & Received. []

# Inmate

My cell has no window,
a small exhaust fan
a commode in the corner.

No calendar or clock.
After every meal,
I tally mark the wall
with charcoal.

They slide in 3 breads
with a bland bottle gourd
every once in a while.

No books to read,
no bits of paper to scribble on.
the low watt tube light
is always on —
can't differentiate
day and night.

They shave my head
once in 3 months. Red ants
are my friends.

Did I say that they shave my head
once in 3 months?

When bored, I stare
at the spider's web,
imagine myself prey. []

# KAROL NIELSEN

## Spring

Spring came as the virus spread and most days I left quarantine at my parents' house in Connecticut to walk through the neighborhood, delighted by blooming magnolias, apples, forsythia, cherries, dogwoods, azaleas, daffodils, bluebells. I watched buds on maples, elms, oaks turn into lush leaves. I counted the walkers, runners, and bikers, about a handful to two dozen, saying hello as I passed by, and I wondered how long it would be before I got back to New York, to the life I had before the pandemic. []

## Cop Shows

We watch cop shows one after another during the long hours of quarantine. CSI: Miami looked good because it starred actors from a favorite series, NYPD Blue. The show opens with a grizzly murder or the discovery of a corpse and the suspects quickly emerge. It's full of beach and pool parties, bloody postmortems, cheesy lines, and unbelievable confessions. Too often I pick up my cellphone and check messages, social media, even the news, and lose the thread. But I always hope that the next episode will draw me in. []

# KATLEY DEMETRIA BROWN

## How to (Temporarily) Forget the Plague

I stay socially distant while swimming
I avoid state parks, beaches, pools,
and any place where there are crowds.
They are magnets for disease.
I don't want to wear a mask at the beach, anyway.
It seems unnatural.

There is a place I know where hardly anyone goes
on the banks of the Connecticut River.
It's quiet with large trees and sunny in the afternoon.
The shore is muddy, not sandy
but I don't care.

Will the water make me sick?
So far it hasn't and I've been swimming there for years
I jump in the water, join the dance of the current
and the waves and
forget that there's a pandemic going on
besides, the sun is out.
The virus, like the Undead, avoids the sun.

It's the shoppers at Aldi that worry me
not the muddy water. []

# Dancing in the Zoom Room

We don't hold hands.
We practice social distancing.
We are boxes on a screen
in rows
five across and five down
when in gallery mode
frustrated folk dancers
who miss human contact.
We dance in whatever space we have at home,
living room, bedroom, kitchen, garage.
Sometimes it's cramped.
We dance together yet apart.
We see old friends in the boxes
and sometimes make new ones.

The sound quality is sometimes terrible.
The lead dancer in the big box
is not always in synch with the music.

Sometimes we talk to each other
when the music isn't playing
more often than not we are muted
when the music is on so we chat in a window
on the side of the screen.

We come from all over the world
to dance in the Zoom Room.
We await the day we can finally hold hands. []

# KELLY NICKIE

## Contained

Within
700 square feet
of
freckled carpet
PVC patio chairs
and two salt lamps
lives my own
chatter
sometimes
relieved
by hand sanitizer

I've been texting
back
and forth
with a bot
that told me
I'm the winner
of a luxury sea cruise

Its positive energy
vaguely amusing

Sharing
Dad jokes
morning yoga affirmations
and flirty innuendo
gets me through
some
of these
days
where
casualties
surpass
our word count []

# LA FELLEMAN

## Heavyhearted

Fitness centers are closed and they
Drive through windows grabbing local
Takeout each day like it contains
Their full patriotic duty

will i recognize anyone
after? []

## Crane Therapy

Calmed by repetitive
Trilling call of Sandhills
Over Crane Cam live feed

We were supposed to be there in person
At sundown when they lifted from corn fields
Thousands swirling seeking shelter below

Congregating to the river safe
In their numbers

Remember sharing that instinct of
Social creatures? []

# LINDA SCHELLER

## Maury

Pale light and the sound of crows drags him
from a dream of a young woman with an axe.
Perhaps she intended to kill him. Perhaps
she carried an axe for her own protection.
Perhaps she'd been chopping wood for a fire
they'd watch together, seated at the edge of heat.
He longs to remain in bed, but the empty pillow
next to his exhales the scent of loss. Sighing,
he rises, back stiff and hips aching.

He brews coffee and stares into the fridge.
No more eggs or bread, cheese almost gone.
Yesterday the radio said he could call a number
and someone would deliver more food.
The radio said too some damned politician
considered him expendable, he and others
unable to work. *Useless.* Maury didn't think
his son felt that way, but they seldom talked.
Ira was busy with his job, presumably happy,
married and living in France. No kids, though.
Miriam had always wanted grandchildren.
If only they'd had more children.
Oh, Miriam. Alone, gasping in that hospital.
He never got to say goodbye, never told her
how much she'd meant to him all those years.
If only…well, no use thinking like that.

He closes the fridge and sits near the radio.
Steam rises from the cup to join the invisible
everywhere. Coffee, a radio, dreams.
So it's come to this. What a life. []

# Jose

Like most children, he thought he hated school
until it wasn't there. Assignments, essays, and tests,
the despicable parts, came now in an online barrage,
but he missed Gerardo and recess soccer games,
the noisy cafeteria and Elena's long braids.

His parents were home all the time now, which was weird.
Sometimes they argued, and his mother would cry,
and then they'd disappear into their bedroom. Later
he'd hear laughter on the other side of their locked door.

He missed shopping with his mother, the narrow aisles
and jumbled shelves, the trapped toys. Here at home
all his toys were boring. Video games bored him.
Everything was different and boring.

One day, his mother taught him to play poker
with dry beans for bets. They dragged the ladder
to the side yard, picked plums, and baked pies.
They built a birdhouse from scraps of wood
and weeded the vegetable garden. His father
showed him how to change the oil, and together
they cleaned the garage. His sister sketched,
and the dog under her desk thumped his tail.

At dusk they lit candles and told ghost stories.
Jose's father tuned his guitar, and they sang
"Bingo," "Clementine," and "Don Gato."
As they slept, the moon poured tender light
through the curtains, and at breakfast
they recounted their dreams as the sun
unveiled another pandemic day. []

# Mandy

At some point last fall her body stopped making money,
her mind stopped making sense. They took her by bus
to Modesto with others hauled from the sidewalks
and lured from the alleys with hot food and cigarettes.

Mandy was a rape baby born poor to a mother born poor,
sheltered and fed by a chain of uncles whose fists
and dicks elicited bruised repayment. The new girl
at dozens of schools, filthy and friendless,
she was 14 when her mother died. Mandy
vanished into the maze of meth and prostitution.

Just before the pandemic, Modesto dismantled the tents,
and most of the homeless returned to the streets.
Mandy's tricks dried up. New flesh attracted johns,
not toothless mumblers leathered and spent at 28.
Shelters and missions, understaffed, overflowed with need.
Between the rain and withdrawals, Mandy couldn't recall
how or why she should care for herself. Cold, sick,
and weary, she walked into the Tuolumne River
and for the last time, unnoticed, disappeared. []

# LITA KURTH

## The Stasis

The gray sky waits
Trees immobile lean like frozen drunks
How do they stay in the same place so long
The only thing that bounces their leaves
is a bird, the only thing up there
that's going somewhere

Flying birds are punctuation
on this sky of immovable prose
silent, though alive
Thank you, birds, for your squeaks and flights

Underground, I know the worms and bugs
mice and moles are moving, walking, eating, copulating
giving birth, ecstatic, celebrating
Up here nothing moves
Not even clouds

A cluster of spring-green leaves
blows gently as if to escape detection
as if tired, restless []

# My Week, April, 2020

My week was made of pedestrian deeds
stepping into the bike lane
when someone on the sidewalk approached
     Weeding: OCD activity for outdoors
     Cooking: OCD activity for indoors
Emptying cat litter into the trash
Pulling clothes from washer to dryer
Using bleach and alcohol
And in the evening, wine.
Deliver us

My week was made of hands on keyboard
eyes on screen
scrubbing a floor, filling ziplock bags
with cloth and Ivory soap
for homeless folks
wearing a mask to the grocery store
trying in vain while wearing gloves
to open a plastic bag
Deliver us

My week was lucky. I worked from home
witnessed only in passing, the heroes and angels
of everyday places:
café clerks and cleaners, cooks and drivers
nurse's aides at old folks' homes and hospitals,
Deliver us
food and medicine
deliver us
to almost-empty airports
deliver us
to crammed emergency rooms

Take a moment with me
now to keep in mind a few: Anil Subba, Uber driver,
New York city; Arcelia Martinez, FoodMaxx clerk,
San Jose; Frank Boccabella III, TSA worker,
Newark Airport; Paul Frishkorn, flight attendant, union member,
Fort Pierce; Israel Tolentino, Jr., Pasaic firefighter;
James Villecco, Staten Island auto mechanic;
Jason Hargrove, driver of a city bus
in Michigan, Detroit.

Deliver their families from destitution
laid on top of grief
and
Deliver from oblivion
And business as usual
And insufficient safety and insufficient pay
those who remain On this day
When Martin Luther King, Jr. passed away []

# LYNN WHITE

## New Times

The birds are singing an opening chorus
for the pollen laden bees to hum
over the flower beds in the park
which buzz as well as bloom.
Summer is in full swing.

But in the playground
the swings are empty,
the marks of courts and pitches
have already faded.
It's deserted now.
Since the lockdown
no one plays outdoors.
None of us play the old games anymore.

There are new rules this summer
as we stay at home
carefully distanced
in our hazy miasma
of enforced laziness
waiting and hoping
that the clouds
hanging over us
will be blown away
before memories fade
with the laughter of children
and the marks on the ground. []

# MARK BLICKLEY

Photography: **Beatrice Georgalidis**

## Gravity Ungrateful

Yes, I am dressed in mourning
Dark clothes for a dark time
Yet I yearn to escape
Pandemic imprisonment
With the germ of an idea
That will allow me to soar
Above my confinement

In an airborne threat
Against complacency and boredom
As I reach up to a blue heaven
That promises social distancing
On a cosmic scale,
But that old bitch gravity
Bears down on me,
Slapping me down
Like a petulant child
Crying out
For what she cannot have,
Slammed back
To a blanketed earth
Of red white and blue. []

# MEG SMITH

## A Widow, Closing

I have been swirling and dancing
in this black veil for some mad time --
the years become me, and I could
fall in the snow with all grace, and laugh.
Above, the stars rush away.
All around me, everything rushes away.
There is now, a season of shrouds,
all riddling with ghosts,
and tears that need not be.
How peopled the world has become with
mad, dancing in funerary masks.
Roses do not pass, and still, we fall. []

## Callery Park

The playgrounds reopened.
yellow sashes falling away,
like young girls twirling in a parade.
Dusk ushered in purple and gray,
and I went, as I always have.
This is my purest hour, opening twilight
on the swingset.
A family soon arrives and set everything
to spinning, creaking, swaying, laughing.
A boy and I made high arcs
between the sandy ground and the sky.
We counted numbers, in Spanish, and English,
before shadows summoned us home --
to masks, doors, the dark balance of days. []

# MEGHA SOOD

## Of Todays and Tomorrows

How will you separate today's and tomorrows
when everything will move blindly
like a hamster on a wheel?
a big ball of unending yarn with no beginning or end
the separation of whites and colored
will not happen so swiftly like before
now it will be either infected or safe

We live to bury our past--
wiping incessantly, tears streaming down
from burying our loved ones
alone in unmarked graves
stashed like a garbage pile
in the refrigerated trucks
our sorrows will carry their deep stench
through our thin veins forever
nothing will be lost to the wind

the closeness, the tactile love
we all are desperately looking
that closeness will be long gone
now every anxious eye will look
for the way out, a sterile haven
anxiety churning a shade darker
by every passing moment

sorrow hidden behind those masks
will hide your pain forever
the eyes, the window to your soul
will now hideaway your loneliness
as you will stand six feet apart in a room
filled with loved ones

rolling nights with its black teeth
will continue to smirk
the contagion sitting boisterously
hiding in the bushes
will be ready to spring at us
at any given moment
while we will be split between
the pain of burying our past
and grieving for the future
we once had. []

# O. YEMI TUBI (MOYAT)

## Lest We Forget

Lest we forget
Our unlikely heroes
As week by week by our doors' steps
With hands, pans and pots applauded
As they answered the call of duty
Gallantly like courageous armies,
With People of commonwealth and foreign born,
With common purpose to serve and protect,
The Queen and the country they love so dear.

Lest we forget
Our unlikely heroes,
Once Overworked, under paid, under valued
Our only forces of defence still they were
On the evil days of pandemic.
Worn out and tired, still they battled on
With little thought of their own safety.
Separated from their loved ones
To save the lives of many.

Lest we forget
The pregnant nurse and the aged doctors
Out of retirements they came
To pay the ultimate price
To deliver many souls
From the jaw of the devourer.
As we continue to honour the living,
Our fallen unlikely heroes
Lest we forget. []

# Humanity Paused

Sometime in March
the world stood still,
humanity placed on pause.
Faces masked and scarved
as sanitized hands slowly dried
and a million people died.
Open borders closed their gates,
land bridges failed to land.
Houses labelled 'social bubbles,'
sat with gates chained shut.
Summer journeys went unwalked,
as Corona bought a first class ticket
and flew across the world. []

# PREKSHA KUKREJA

## Engineering Project in a Pandemic

The cool crackle of untouched plastic,
the silky sheen of black satin packed within,
a crowd of thousands- my sister's pinch
pulls me five months back
and into the present.

*Somewhere in China, a novel coronavirus is detected.*

Will it be arthritis or stretchers?
Plantar fasciitis or hot flashes?
My team gears up to change healthcare
with our senior design project.

*The novel coronavirus makes entry into the United States.*

Scribbling new circuit schematics every hour,
we run out of room on the whiteboard walls
as we spend yet another night
perfecting our pitch with high ambition
and bad coffee for company.

*Italy experiences a sudden surge in cases.*

Transistor values, Arduino choices,
wearability, the debates drone on.
A month into the semester
and the campus environment
is heating up like the tiny resistors
on my circuit board.

*Next door, the CDC declares a public health emergency.*

We rip apart the half-built circuit,
fight to take home the design sketches
that have been demoted. Mere souvenirs
of a graduation cut short.

*Stay-at-home orders are issued around the globe.*

My mother's tea replaces the college coffee
that my memory refuses to concede was bitter.
Zoom becomes the new design lab,
and we try to build a virtual circuit,
whoever heard of such a thing.

*The world seems to regress a hundred years,*
*as days of the Spanish flu are recounted.*

Fourteen days of isolation
and boredom burns blisters
into my brain. My resistors
look forlorn, as if they too
miss the shiny new oscilloscope
from the design lab.

*Washington sees 22 deaths in a senior care home.*

I pray for those in Washington,
those unable to see their parents,
those unable to come home
to their children. Every morning, I pray
before fumbling with my circuit board again. []

# RICH LARSON

## Love in the Time of Coronavirus

Vinohradska is breezy and sintered
with sunshine. This is Prague,
shedding winter. This is me,
shedding winter, serotonin coaxed
by warm clear skies.

I'm a cliché, so I see her: black felt coat,
ash blonde hair, snow white AirPods.

She crosses the tram tracks, and traffic
stops, and I take her wake
because the hook behind my belly
says I should say something.

I say, your coat looks very Russian.
She says, Belarusian.

Her eyes are smoked glass
while I spill my guts, asking stupid
questions and babbling
in the way that only works
with spring-time hormones in play.

Her name is Nastya; we knock elbows
instead of shaking hands.

---

That night my sister is on lunch-break
when I call her. I hear backdrop
noise from Jasper Ave, a hemisphere away,
as she hunts for Indian fast-food.

She wants to talk COVID, and I admit
my primate brain just isn't worried,
because I just met this girl

who came to Prague to be a musician
and gives me leather-winged bats
instead of butterflies.

My sister says her conferences are cancelled
and Kiran is immunodeficient
and our grandmother is ninety-two, so
now is not the time to eat bats

and I should pull my primate brain
back out of my primate ass.
Love you, talk soon.

---

Czech class is taught by a substitute,
since Misha is home *nemocna*,
and our class of eight is only three.

We learn about the weather, like how to say
Vinohradska is rain-drenched
and empty today. Afterwards I hurry
with my hood up, to the Step In cafe.

Nastya arrives under a black umbrella,
folds it away, ignores me
to chat with the owner in Czech
about nothing I understand
until *vegan cheesecake*.

Then we sit and caffeinate; she says
I look like someone who writes about space
and maybe writes poems.

I ask her where she would go
if there were free flights, no coronavirus;
she says China, because of Taoism
and because she likes paying for street food

by scanning a QR code
on a rumpled piece of paper.

The cheesecake comes. I compare the calluses
on her guitar-scarred fingertips. We make a pact
to wash our hands well and to

not enter any coughing contests,
no matter how big the prize money.

---

That night my grandmother
doesn't quite know my voice
when I call her landline from Gmail.

She is moving from one side of the lodge,
assisted living, to the other side,
barely living, after two weeks in hospital
reading the same German poetry
over and over.

She says she is ready to go; she says it
often now. I help her to remember
the things we like remembering:

Walking around the pond in summer,
taking the shortcut down the grassy ditch
where she gathered momentum --
*Der Schwung* --
to push herself up the other side
on stiffening legs.

We go back through memories
all the way to the village where she grew up:
Schonau, which no longer exists
except for a single cabbage field.

She says she remembers every person,
every neighbor, every neighbor's child
who is dead now from the war
or from eighty years of afterwar.

Her voice is heavy again, and I know
she's a romantic, so I tell her
about Nastya: us hurrying together to Muzeum
under her bobbing black umbrella,
arms linked.

The taut moment between us,
like the string of her electric guitar
or maybe the violin she
both loved and hated as a child.

How we came so close to kissing
before we knocked elbows
and I descended into a metro
full of facemasks, and she went off
into the rain.

My grandmother tells me to write a poem.
I tell her not to die until summertime.
Love you, talk soon. []

# RICHARD C. ENOS

## Crown of Leaves

Great tree, crown of leaves, you tower over me.
What have you seen in history?
Natives rushing past you chasing game.
Pioneers building fires with your twigs,
wagons rolling west toward the roiling sea.
An outlaw trips over you, fleeing justice's fate.
Innocent lives dangle from your branches.
You stand with us today, defiant and free.
Thunder snarls, but true power is a tree. []

# ROBERT ALLEN

## Snot

It fired at me
a spittle of phlegm,
wet and vile
a spit in the eye
from God and disease.
Covid-19
burst like
a bubble
of snot
a night time
moan
a hot rattle
of lungs.
We heal or die
with a soft brittle cough
and purely alone. []

# DR. RON CRAIG

## Lockdown Blues: A Senryu Sequence

under cover of darkness
we unload
the TP

lockdown
refusing to set foot on
the scale

an infection of
virus fears
lockdown blues

washing
all grocery items
KP duty

pandemic
I put the brakes
on breaking news

unsure
of his intentions
masked face

covid
makes its rounds
the wheels on the bus

donning and doffing PPE
an ER light switch
shorts out

four hundred years
even the virus
discriminates

gridiron
gained and lost ground
pandemic season

all this virus bullshit
I pop him
another Corona

positive stats
for the pandemic
*Play ball!*

respect for others
no TP-ing
this Halloween

corona virus
in 20-20 hindsight
more TP

forgetting the pandemic
early morning
birdsong []

# SANCHARI CHATTERJEE

## To the isolated souls

There are a thousand stars but only one
                 shines bright for you.
There are so many waves to drown you,
But one sea rock to give you a shore.
There are many sinners to commit more sin
And there is you like a changing hymn
Accepting your flaws, keeping them in mind.
You strive and strive and not once yield
Go on my friend, for it is a battle field.
You are isolated, cut off from all.
Remember, like a raven in grief, like a maiden in a desert
Like a rainbow among clouds, like a reflection in a mirror
You have been pure.
You have seen the best of the Times
And now are seeing the worst of it.
Keep unraveling to the world
                 your potential, your courage, your creativity,
'Cause if this talent goes unnoticed
That will be a real pity. []

# SOUMYADEEP ROY

## A Second Chance During The Lockdown

Why your dollars, pounds, rupees
Seem so frustrated?
What happened to your pride of wealth and knowledge?
Why they look so disappointed?
What's wrong with your habits, now?
Why are they more concerned about the health
Rather than the wealth?
Why are you so afraid of the frowning of the time?
As if you're about to atone
For all your evil deeds that count a thousand tonne.
If all your queries are lost in the echo of your cacophony
Then it's time, I guess
It's time to watch her managing her symphony
It's time to watch her taking her revenge.
Look out the window and see
She's healing by killing all the odds
Just see
How she's reviving her streams of Apah and Agni.
How she's sparing us the quarantine
To free all our guilt
To resuscitate our dead ethics.
May be now she's giving us a second chance during the lockdown
To rejuvenate all her organs
That we've burnt down. []

# SUBHRANIL MAHATO

## Sisyphean

Am I sad?
Or am I happy?
I don't know.
What is this turmoil
Of passive existence?

"Why do you get out of bed
In the morning?"

"I don't know."

It's a lie,
I do know.

Getting out of bed
Is a task of Sisyphus.

Never-ending
Never truly accomplished.

What other choice
Do I have? []

# A Portrait of a Rainy Day
# during Quarantine

The ponds ripple with rain
As I celebrate my mother's birthday.
No one seems to complain about
Weather anymore, as we all smile
From five feet away under our umbrellas,
Or simply allowing our hands to wet.
I was waiting for the rain to stop,
To tilt my face to the sun
Like a daffodil. []

# SUCHITA PARIKH-MUNDUL

## living history

erect as many monuments
as you like;
fabricate the pastor tear it down;
replace it with a new format;
whichever way you calibrate
the compass,
the wormhole of time
will not narrow to a pinpoint
of a second that could easily
skip past you in the intake
of a breath.
a forgotten fact will definitely
eat its way to the centre
and corrode your insides;
time is now a leisurely gent
who will wait
until the ladies have sung
an operetta at dawn's
endless expanse;
hush now to hear
the world creaking,
to hear unlucky souls
dying, to hear the clock
ticking ever so languidly
towards you;
there is no escape
but to plunder
and wait. []

# Headlines

...India...
bleeding valleys,
swallowing lines,
pustuled friction,
dystrophic justice,
convulse, coagulate,
ash and descent,
time for penitence.

...West...
haemorrhaging lies,
political murk,
ocular tricks,
oratory slips,
cementing, whitewashing,
Guernica and Skrik,
licenced spies.

...world...
cystic intentions,
miasmic truths,
indelible voices,
shattered spines,
occult, occident,
façade and exposure,
eviscerated pasts.

...women...
eager asters,
dimpled daffodils,
smothered stems,
twisted vines,
choke, strangle,
rape and murder,
no arrests.

...individuals...
blank shot, riot,
protest, injustice,
politics, death,
pandemic, death,
poverty, death,
death, death,
forget, forget,
all dead. []

# SUEANN WELLS

## Uncertainty

I want what I cannot have
Right now
Job security
Future certainty
A steady paycheck
Teaching
Doing what I love
It'll be online
Distant
Different
Not terrible
Kinda cool with students on board
This uncertainty
Unknowing
Is killing me
I shouldn't complain
I still have a paycheck
For a few weeks anyway
And when that's gone
I'm not winning bread anyway
Some lost jobs outright
Need to feed their families on nothing
Some didn't have savings to begin with
We'll be okay
I'll be okay
But the uncertainty rips us apart []

# SUPARNA CHAUDHURY RIJHWANI

## Slow Down...

The world it still spins.
The sun it still shines and the trees have flowers.
Yet, for me the world stands still,
No sound, no movement just as if a heavy curtain
                                    has draped my window.

The pandemic rages on outside.
Destroying the very fabric of human existence, social bonding.
No touching, no hugging, no physical interaction.
No planning for holidays, no visiting friends and families.
No stepping out of the house unnecessarily.
The list is endless.

Like cutting off the wings of a butterfly,
Life sits heavy and hard on my shoulders
As a deep pain of missing my family engulfs me.
The road ahead unclear, the path filled with shadows.

Yet, there is light outside.
Dolphins have been spotted in the canals of Venice.
The Great Barrier Reef seems to be rejuvenating.
There are ducks swimming freely in the creek.
Sharks are spotted near the coastline.

Nature has a different story to tell.
Nature seems to be enjoying the much-needed
                                    respite from humankind.
Nature seems to be sending a message to us,
'Slow down and let us heal!'

Like every cloud with a silver lining,
It is clear that our actions have hurt our surroundings.

That our relentless pursuit of wants has created
                        an imbalance in the cosmos.
That we humans have been innately selfish.

The perspective is what this pandemic provides,
That for our existence and our future, that to repair the damage,
We need to stay in and slow down!
Time is the best healer
Patience is the key.

I get up to part the curtains of my window,
A sliver of light filters in.
It is time to embrace that light
And fill my heart with hope. []

# VANDANA KUMARI JENA

## Survival

When Covid comes calling
changing lives irrevocably
without prior warning
So many untold
die on the parched lips
of migrant workers
who return home
as opportunities dry
Shops are shuttered
and factories shut
People are locked within
Prisoners though not
Of their own making
I chip away the mold
from a loaf of bread
and eat it with a cup of chai
made from milk gone sour
Quarantined because
my neighbors
turned Covid Positive
All five of them
The very day
I had planned to go out
and shop
I starve in my one room tenement
rummaging for
half-eaten packets of biscuits
stale peanuts
and Maggi noodles
way beyond the expiry date
How long can I last without food?
Not fourteen days surely?
The tv works

Thank God
My mind will be fed
even when my body starves
I am saddened
to learn of 16 men
who lay on railway tracks
on their journey home on foot
for a few hours respite
secure in the knowledge
that trains don't run
during the lockdown
and slumbered on
as the goods train
thundered along
trampling them
and their dreams
I watch
a toddler
prancing around her mother
on a railway platform
pulling away the coverlet
covering her
in an impromptu game
of hide and seek
Not knowing that
the one who lay prone
was her mother no longer
but her corpse
Death knocks at my door too
I murmur
Not Covid
But starvation
I wonder if I can live
another day without food

when I hear a knock
Is that death knocking?
I wonder
I open the door
just as lit
and find a food hamper
a hot cooked meal
a gift
left by a NGO no doubt
Overwhelmed
I wonder
If it is
the last meal offered
to a condemned prisoner
before execution
Or is it a portend of
happier days to come? []

# ZÉLIA DE SOUSA

## My Bus Stop Sun-Tan

Lock-down - Still not been lifted?
I'm white as snow - I want to be golden-brown.
The sun is out – how to get a tan?

Feeling the sunon my naked flesh.
Wearing shorts, a sleeveless top, flip-flops, sun glasses
                              -sitting at the bus stop.

Loving it.

'Excuse me miss?' Say's the police officer in his van.
                              'Where are you going?'
'To obtain essentials'
'May I ask what?'
'Vitamin D'

The bus arrives – I hop on – I need a break from the heat –
                              it's a little too hot.

I get off the next stop.

By the time lock-down is up.
I will be golden-brown. []

# If I Choose To Die Today

Family-
If I choose to die today, will you care?

Work –
How quickly will you replace me?

Friends –
Will you miss me?

Hobby classes –
Will you notice I wasn't there?

Public transport drivers –
Will you ask my whereabouts?

Bank –
How quickly will you try to take over my account?

Corner shop –
Will you bring your prices down, hoping I will come back?

Landlord –
Will you steal my belongings?

Hospital –
Will you sleep at night knowing you did all you could?

Morgue –
Will I just be another dead body?

Places of worship –
Will I go to heaven, even though…I... well that's between me and god.

Eulogy speech –
Please, those are crocodile tears.

Will –
Can't wait to see the look on your faces-I left you nothing.

…'What are you smiling about?' I ask my shrink via Zoom
thanks to the 2020 pandemic.

'I won't let any of the above happen.'

'Why, so you can get more money off me?'

'It's working isn't it?' []

# POET BIOGRAPHIES

**ALAN PERRY** is a US poet and author of the chapbook, *Clerk of the Dead* , published by Main Street Rag Publishing in 2020. His poems have appeared in *Tahoma Literary Review, Heron Tree, Sleet Magazine* , *Gyroscope Review, Zingara Poetry Review* and elsewhere, and in several anthologies. He is a Senior Poetry Editor for *Typehouse Literary Magazine* , and was nominated for Best of the Net. Alan holds a BA in English from the University of Minnesota, and he and his wife divide their time between Minneapolis, Minnesota and Tucson, Arizona, USA.
More at: https://alanperrypoetry.com

**ANN PRIVATEER** is a poet, artist, and photographer. Some of her work has appeared in Third Wednesday and Entering to name a few. She grew up in the Midwest and now lives in Northern California.

**BAISALI CHATTERJEE DUTT** is a former columnist for 'Mother & Baby'. She has also compiled and edited two volumes of 'Chicken Soup for the Indian Soul' series "On Friendship" and "Brothers and Sisters". She has written "Sharbari Datta: The Design Diva". Her poetry has been published in various anthologies and magazines like "Veils, Shackles and Halos", "For Rhinoceros in a Shrinking World", "Algebra of Owls", "Femina", "The Asian Age" & others. Baisali has performed with some of the country's top English theatre groups. Currently she is the Course Consultant at The Creative Arts Studio, and drama teacher at Sri Sri Academy.

**BHISMA UPRETI** is a Nepali poet, essayist and novelist of high repute. 19 books (9 books of poetry, 9 books of essays/travels and one Novel) of his have been published. Many of his works have been translated into English, Hindi, Korean, Serbian, Slovenian, Japanese, Sinhala and others. He has represented Nepal in many international literary conclaves in Asia and Europe. A Gold medalist of National Poetry Festival organized by

Nepal Academy, Upreti is also recipient of prestigious awards like SAARC Literature Award, Gopal Prasad Rimal Rastriya Kavya Puraskar, Uttam Shanti Puraskar, Yuva Varsha Moti Puraskar, Shankar Lamichhane Youth Essay Award and many more. Mr. Upreti is currently the secretary of PEN Nepal.

**DR. BRAJESH KUMAR GUPTA "MEWADEV"** is a recipient of the Presidency of the International Prize De Finibus Terrae in memory of Maria Monteduro (Italy). He has been awarded an honorary doctorate from The Institute of the European Roma Studies. He has received Uttar Pradesh Gaurav Samman 2019. Presently he acts as the Secretary-General of The World Union of Poets. He is the author of 6 books and is an assistant professor at Eklvaya P.G. College, Banda.

**CHRISTIAN GARDUNO** edited the compilation Evolver and his own solo poetry collection Face, while a History undergraduate at the University of California, Berkeley. His work can be read in over 35 literary magazines, including Riza Press, where his poem, "The Return", was a Finalist in their 2019 Poetry & Art Contest. He lives and writes in South Texas.

**COLLEEN MOYNE** is a published freelance writer living in the lovely riverside town of Mannum in South Australia. She has won several awards for her poetry and has had poems and short stories published in over twenty different anthologies. Her first solo collection, "Time Like Coins' was released in January 2019 by Ginninderra Press. Visit www.colleenmoyne.com

**DIMPLE D. MAPARI** is an Asst. Prof. of English in Shankarlal Khandelwal Arts, Science and Commerce College, Akola. Her areas of interest are Indian Writing in English, criticism, colonial literature, feminism and English Language Teaching. She has published and presented over 25 research papers in Journals, Conferences and seminars of National and International repute and has edited two books.

**DONNA NEMMERS**, a native Iowan, is a wife, mom, gardener, hobby cook, and poet. Having spent over 30 years in the publishing field, she now reserves time for arranging flowers, ingredients, and words. Recently, her poem "Iris" was selected as winner in the International Dylan Thomas Day 2020 Poetry Competition; printed in Hope—a collection of 30 poems published by *Infinity Books UK*.

**DONNY WINTER** is a LGBTQIA+ activist, YouTube blogger, and poet from Saginaw, Michigan. He currently teaches Creative Writing at

Delta College and has publications in the Central Review, Flypaper Magazine, and Sonder Midwest. His forthcoming first full-length collection of poems, Carbon Footprint, will be published by Alien Buddha Press in September 2020.

**DREW PISARRA** is the author of *Publick Spanking*, a collection of short stories published by Future Tense Books, and *Infinity Standing Up*, a collection of queer love sonnets published by Capturing Fire. He is also a recent recipient of a literary grant from the Cafe Royal Cultural Foundation.

**ED O'CASEY** attended the University of North Texas and New Mexico State University. He is the author of the book *Proximidad: A Mexican/American Memoir* and other transformations that have appeared or are upcoming in *Berkeley Poetry Review*, *Cold Mountain Review*, *Tulane Review*, *Euphony*, *Poetry Quarterly*, *Whiskey Island*, and *NANO Fiction*. He lives in San Antonio, Texas.

**EDILSON AFONSO FERREIRA**, 76 years old, is a Brazilian poet who writes in English rather than in Portuguese. Widely published in selected international journals in print and online, he began writing at age 67, after retiring as a bank employee. Nominated for The Pushcart Prize 2017, his first Poetry Collection, Lonely Sailor, One Hundred Poems, was launched in London, in November of 2018. He is always updating his works at www.edilsonmeloferreira.com.

**EMILIAN LUNGU** is a Romanian poet who has recently graduated from University of Babeş-Bolyai, Faculty of Letters, where he majored in Norwegian Language and Literature and minored in Spanish Language and Literature, and is currently doing a Master degree on Visual Art Studies at CESI, University of Bucharest, while on the side taking History of Art and Gender Studies classes from University of Oslo.

**GEORGE R. ROSS / VICTORIA CRAWFORD**: Their poems have appeared in Braided Way and Active Muse and ColdNoon. They both have individually written poems in several other journals. Their perspectives are those of the vulnerable as they are 81 and 70 and are both diabetic. George lives in Boston, MA, while Victoria is retired in Thailand.

**H.L. DOWLESS** is a national & international academic/ESL Instructor. He has been a writer for over thirty years. His latest publications have been two books of non-fiction with Algora Publishing, and fictional publications with combo e-zines and print magazines; Leaves Of Ink, Short Story

Lovers, The Fear Of Monkeys, and Frontier Tales.

**HILARY KING**'s poems have appeared in *Fourth River, Belletrist, SWIMM, PANK, The Cortland Review, Blue Fifth Review, Sky Island Journal, and other publications.* She is the author of the book of poems, *The Maid's Car.* Originally from Virginia, she has been quarantined in the San Francisco Bay Area with her husband, two children, one dog, one cat, and one sourdough starter.

**HOWIE GOOD** is the author of *The Death Row Shuffle*, a poetry collection forthcoming from Finishing Line Press.

**JANE CARTER**: After a 30+ year career in the Civil Service, she retired last year. Despite only having experience in writing statistical reports and emails, she decided to try her hand at fiction and joined Newport Writers in January 2020. She hadn't written poetry since school (a long time ago) but somehow the emotions around lockdown inspired her to write her first one – *The Stolen Sun* within the first weeks of being stuck at home. Following that she wrote a poem every couple of weeks throughout this time.

**JARED MORNINGSTAR** is a high school English teacher and adjunct English professor. He loves to write poetry and short stories that reflect his interests and his observations of the world. In addition to literature, Morningstar loves music, playing guitar, late night diner experiences, and long road trips. He lives in Michigan with his wife and children.

**JAY GANDHI** is a thirty-four year old poet residing in Mumbai, India. He's an Accountant by profession, a Guitarist and a Yoga Practitioner. He derives inspiration from mundane things. Poetry is his tool to find beauty in the daily routine. His poetry has been featured in anthologies such as *Persian Sugar in English Tea, Poets on the Run, Saffron Flavoured Rock Candy* and *Once upon a meal.* His poems have been published by the online magazine *Muddy River Poetry Review* and have made it to the front page of *PoetryCircle.com.* In free time, Jay likes to walk for long distances.

**KAROL NIELSEN** is the author of the memoirs Black Elephants (Bison Books, 2011) and Walking A&P (Mascot Books, 2018) and the chapbooks This Woman I Thought I'd Be (Finishing Line Press, 2012) and Vietnam Made Me Who I Am (Finishing Line Press, 2020). Her first memoir was shortlisted for the William Saroyan International Prize for Writing in nonfiction in 2012. Her full poetry collection was a finalist for the Colorado Prize for Poetry in 2007. Her work has appeared in Epiphany, Guernica, Lumina, North Dakota Quarterly, Permafrost, RiverSedge, and elsewhere.

She has taught writing at New York University and New York Writers Workshop.

**KATLEY DEMETRIA BROWN** was born in New York City and grew up in the South Bronx. Her work has been published in a number of Internet and print publications including *Inequitudes*, *Hawai'i Review*, the Culture Cult anthology *Nocturne* and in the series of anthologies: *The Art of Being Human*. She currently lives in Springfield, Massachusetts with her husband and Munchie, the cat. The cat keeps her company late at night while she writes poetry on the computer and listens to Bulgarian folk music.

**KELLY NICKIE** enjoys finding mundane objects and phrases of the everyday, and turning them into second thoughts. Her work has been published in iō Literary Journal, The Broken Spine, Resistance, Door = Jar, Juice, Generation, Synaeresis, The Curious Element, and in the Winnipeg Free Press.

**LA FELLEMAN** is currently an accountant at the University of Iowa. Before that, she was a seminary professor. Prior to that, she was a pastor. She moved to Iowa City with her husband in 2016 and started writing poetry soon afterwards. In order to learn this new craft, LA attends the Free Generative Writing Workshops. To give back to the local writing community, she organizes a writers open mic at the public library (or via Zoom during pandemics) and serves on the Advisory Council of Iowa City Poetry.

**LINDA SCHELLER** is the author of *Fierce Light* (FutureCycle Press, 2017.) Publishing credits include *The American Journal of Poetry*, *Wisconsin Review*, *Slipstream*, *Hawaii Pacific Review*, *Poem*, and *Connecticut River Review*, with new work forthcoming in *Teach. Write.* and *West Trade Review*. Now retired from teaching, she serves on the board of the Modesto-Stanislaus Poetry Center and programs for KCBP community radio. Her website is lindascheller.com.

**LITA KURTH** MFA- Rainier Writers Workshop, has published in three genres. "Are We Not Ladies," was nominated by *Watershed Review* for Best of the Net, 2017 and "Fish Genesis" was nominated by *Rabid Oak* for a 2019 Best of the Net award. "This is the Way We Wash the Clothes," (CNF) won the 2014 Diana Woods Memorial Award (*Lunchticket*). Her creative nonfiction "Pivot," and short story, "Gardener's Delight" (Dragonfly Press DNA) were nominated for Pushcart Prizes. She is a co-founder of San Jose's literary series, Flash Fiction Forum.

**LYNN WHITE** lives in north Wales. Her work is influenced by issues of social justice and events, places and people she has known or imagined. She is especially interested in exploring the boundaries of dream, fantasy. She was shortlisted in the Theatre Cloud 'War Poetry for Today' competition and has been nominated for a Pushcart Prize and a Rhysling Award. Her poetry has appeared in many publications including: Apogee, Firewords, Peach Velvet, Light Journal and So It Goes.
Find Lynn at: https://lynnwhitepoetry.blogspot.com

**MARK BLICKLEY** is a proud member of the Dramatists Guild and PEN American Center. His latest book is *'Dream Streams,'* a text-based art collaboration with Amy Bassin. https://www.claresongbirdspub.com/featured-authors/amy-bassin-mark-blickley

**BEATRICE GEORGALIDIS** is the executive director of New York's Bright Hill Press, a literary art center and gallery. She has worked for more than twenty years in film and television as a writer, producer and videographer for many companies including Sundance Channel, MTV, VH1.

**MEG SMITH** is a writer, journalist, dancer and events producer, living in Lowell, Mass., USA. Her poetry and fiction have appeared in The Cafe Review, Poetry Bay, Dark Dossier, Sirens Call, and many more. She has contributed to recent anthologies including, Poetry in the Plague Year. She is the author of five poetry books; her short fiction collection, The Plague Confessor, is due out in fall 2020 from Emu Books. She welcomes visits to megmsithwriter.com.

**MEGHA SOOD** is an Assistant Poetry Editor for the UK based Arts and Literary Journal MookyChick. Over 450+ works in journals including Better than Starbucks, Gothamist. Poetry Society of New York, WNYC Studios, Kissing Dynamite etc. Three-time State-level Winner NAMI Dara Axelrod NJ Poetry Contest 2018/2019/2020.National Winner Spring Robinson Lit Prize 2020, Adelaide Literary Award 2019 and Erbacce Prize 2020, Nominated for the iWomanGlobalAwrads 2020, Currently co-editing an anthology celebrating the 100 years of the Woman's suffrage movement in the US. She blogs at meghasworldsite.wordpress.com

**O. YEMI TUBI (MOYAT)** is a Nigerian born, American trained Artist, who currently resides in the United Kingdom. O. Yemi's works was awarded 1st, 2nd, 4th, 5th and 6th places in political commentaries in American Art Awards from 2014 to 2017. He was recipient of Golden Award in 2014 Master of Art International exhibition by Margarita Feaks

Gallery, UK. He also received First Round Award in Art Olympia 2015 International Open exhibition in Tokyo, Japan. O. Yemi's works have been published in Newspapers, Magazines and art books. O. Yemi is a member of the International Association of Visual Artists, Fine Art America, the Society of All Artists, AERA – the Association Embracing Realistic Art, Langley Arts Council and WCA - World Citizen Artists. Visit https://www.o-yemi-tubi.pixels.com

**P.J. REED** is an award winning multi-genre author with books ranging from high fantasy, horror, to haiku. She writes the Richard Radcliffe Paranormal Investigations series and the Bad Decisions series. Reed is also the editor and chief paranormal investigator for the Exmoor Noir newsletter. Reed lives in Devon, England with her two daughters, two rescue dogs, and one feral cat called Sammy. Visit pjreedwriting.wixsite.com/horror OR pjreedwriting.wixsite.com/poetry OR pjreedwriting.wixsite.com/fantasy

**PREKSHA KUKREJA** is a biomedical engineer and amateur poet. She graduated from Georgia Institute of Technology in the spring of 2020 at the height of the COVID-19 pandemic and hopes to document her experiences as an engineer and researcher in the form of poetry.

**RICH LARSON** was born in Galmi, Niger, has lived in Canada, USA, and Spain, and is now based in Prague, Czech Republic. He is the author of the novel Annex and the collection Tomorrow Factory, which contains some of the best of his 150+ published stories. His work has been translated into Polish, Czech, Bulgarian, Romanian, Portuguese, French, Italian, Vietnamese, Chinese and Japanese.

**RICHARD C. ENOS** is a writer and software engineer based in Houston. He will have poems published in September in April Murphy's humorous picture book, *COVID-19 in Three to Five Words: A Visual History.*

**ROBERT ALLEN** lives and loves in Northern California where he writes poetry, takes long walks, and looks at birds. His work has been published in The Behind the Mask Anthology, Alien Buddha Press, Persephone's Daughters, Pensive Stories, The Daily Drunk, and Writer's Egg Magazine.

**DR. RON CRAIG** is a retired psychology professor living in Batavia, Ohio, USA. Since 2016 his haiku and senryu have been published in numerous edited journals, anthologies and blogs. As an Ohio Certified Volunteer Naturalist he practices stewardship at the Cincinnati Nature Center. He is married with one adult daughter.

**SANCHARI CHATTERJEE** is an M.A in English and Culture study. She likes observing human behaviour, cultural specificity and exploring new places. Her dream is to become a writer.

**SOUMYADEEP ROY** is a poet from India

**SUBHRANIL MAHATO** is currently working as a Research Scholar in the Department of English in Sidho Kanho Birsha University, Purulia (West Bengal), India. Besides taking interests in cinema, literature and music, he has also fascination for monsoon, nature-walk and long-drive in free time. He can be reached through mahato.subhranil@gmail.com.

**SUCHITA PARIKH-MUNDUL** is a Mumbai-based freelance writer and copy editor whose poems have been published in Sahitya Akademi's Indian Literature, Muse India and Cerebration. A debut collection of poetry titled 'Liquid Apnea' was published by Sampark, Kolkata in 2005. Her recent accolades include winning first place in a local poetry tournament and a runner-up position in a national poetry competition.

**SUEANN WELLS** is a freelance writer/editor and adjunct English professor in western NY. Sueann Wells writes to share her perspective on the world and loves to celebrate the natural, the human, the positive, even as this world turns upside down for each of us on the rollercoaster of life. May we all rise up by sharing our voices. Sueann's creative and professional writing has been published widely, and a sampling of her foray in editing/publishing are available via Lulu.

**SUPARNA CHAUDHURY RIJHWANI** is a writer, a traveller and an educator. She is also the founder/creator of her online magazine Festive Riot, which has till date published 6 issues. She blogs and writes when life permits her.

**VANDANA KUMARI JENA** is a retired civil servant by profession and is a writer by inclination. She has published over 200 middles in leading newspapers in India. Her stories have been published in over 25 anthologies. She has published two novels 'The Dance of Death' (2008) and 'Clueless' (2019), three collection of short stories, 'The Incubation Chamber' (2014) 'The Future is Mine' (2015) and 'One Rotten Apple and Other Stories' (2018) as well as a collection of middles, 'In the Middle' (2015). Her poems have been published in several anthologies.

**ZÉLIA DE SOUSA** is a Portuguese/South African now living in the United Kingdom. Brazilian Author Paulo Coelho inspired her to write after reading The Alchemist. She likes to write long/short stories, poetry and scripts. Zélia loves travelling and turning her adventures into stories. Her work has been published in Anthologies, Anti-Heroin Chic Magazine & Another Chicago Magazine. She has contributed to The Loneliness publishing magazine project and is acknowledged in the memoir The True Adventures of Gidon Lev: A Holocaust Survivor.

Made in the USA
Coppell, TX
06 August 2021